MW00436065

Guided Report Writing

Table of Contents

Using *Guided Report Writing*

Guided Report Writing provides a framework for teaching students how to write a report. Students learn to locate information from a variety of sources and then synthesize that information into an organized report. This guided practice is an important step toward successful independent report writing.

Steps in Writing a Report

Pages 3–12 provide an explanation of an eight-step process you will use to conduct each report writing lesson. The eight steps are as follows:

Choosing a Topic
Formulating Subtopics
Locating Information
Taking Notes
Converting Notes to Paragraphs
Revising, Responding, Editing
Producing the Final Copy
Including Additional Materials

On page 13 there is a Report Conference Form for evaluating a report. This form may be used in teacher-student conferences or by students as a self-evaluation.

Guided Lessons

The lessons on pages 14–91 provide everything you need to guide your students in writing 10 different reports. Each lesson includes the following:
- step-by-step teacher directions
- several reproducible information sources—mock magazine, newspaper, and encyclopedia articles; posters, graphs, maps, time lines, and a science investigation
- a note taker
- a final report form

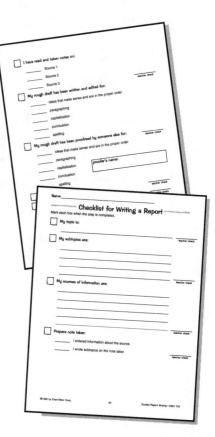

Independent Report Writing

When students are ready to begin their own research, reproduce the Checklist for Writing a Report on pages 92 and 93. Students can then move through the same eight-step process independently with periodic teacher checks.

Eight Steps in Writing a Report

1 Choosing a Topic

A topic can be any subject. It might be an animal, a place, a person, or an idea. Beginning report writers often choose very broad topics that cannot be addressed completely. For example, "African Animals" is too broad, while "Giraffes" is more manageable. "Abraham Lincoln" would be a difficult topic to address in a short report, but "The Childhood of Abraham Lincoln" is doable. An important part of learning how to write a report is learning to choose an appropriate topic.

Know	Want to Know	Learned
There are many kinds of gum.	How did gum come to be?	
People have chewed gum for a long time.	What's gum made of?	

2 Formulating Subtopics

Subtopics are divisions of the topic. One good way to identify subtopics is to think about the information needed to understand the topic. Here are three ways to do that:

• Use a KWL (Know, Want to Know, Learned) chart to think of information that is already known and the information that is needed. List the information on the chart. Organize the entries in the columns into several groups. Give each group a descriptive name. The group names become the subtopics.

• Develop specific categories of information for topics. Discuss the types of information that relate to a specific topic. To learn about an animal it is important to know about the animal's *appearance,* its *habitat,* its *feeding habits,* and its *enemies.* Record the categories discussed as subtopics—appearance, habitat, feeding habits, enemies.

• List questions that address a topic. Organize the questions into groups. Label each group. The labels become the subtopics.

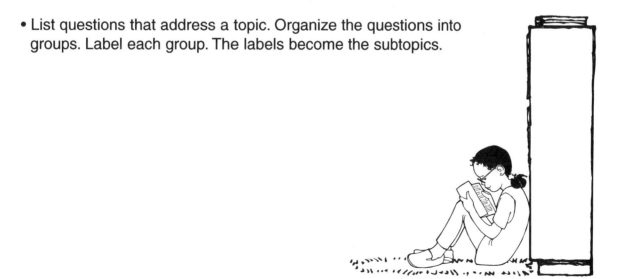

Troubleshooting

At this point in the report writing process, you and your students may face some common problems. Here are some suggestions for solving those problems:

Common Problems Involving Topics

Problem: Your topic is too big!
Solution: Try focusing on one subtopic as the topic and generate new subtopics.

Problem: Your topic is too narrow.
Solution: Think about how the topic relates to a broader category.

Common Problems Involving Subtopics

Problem: You have overlooked an important subtopic.
Solution: Add the subtopic. It's not too late.

Problem: There isn't enough information on a subtopic.
Solution: Change or remove the subtopic.

3 Locating Information

This is the Information Age! There is abundant information available to everyone! Help your students identify information sources that they can use. Model using different types of sources. The information provided in this book will include articles, posters, graphs, tables, and charts.

Places	People	Things
classroom resources	parents	encyclopedias
school library	teachers	books
public library	librarians	magazines
historical societies	experts on the topic	newspapers
museums		television
businesses		Internet
		CD-ROMs
		movies and laser discs

4 Taking Notes

Notes are one way to record information. Note-taking is not a simple skill. It is important to model how to identify key words in a sentence or paragraph and have students practice this before expecting them to take notes independently.
• Emphasize the need to write only the words and phrases that are needed to be clear.
• Do not write in complete sentences during this step.

This simple four-step procedure will make note-taking easy:
1. Read or listen to the information carefully.
2. Decide which subtopic the information addresses.
3. Record key words and phrases under that subtopic.
4. Repeat with other information for other subtopics.

Troubleshooting

Common Problem Involving Note-taking

Problem: Two sources disagree.
Solution:
    • Evaluate the sources carefully.
      Ask: Is one source likely to have more reliable information than the other?
      Will one source have biased information?
      Is one source more current than the other?
    • Do further research to see which opinion is the most accepted or most current.
      If the discrepancy is not resolved, explain it in the report.

5 Converting Notes to Paragraphs

This step involves synthesizing the information on the note taker into a written report. Be sure to address the ideas of organization and topic sentences at this point. A minilesson on organizing information is given below. A minilesson on topic sentences begins on page 9.

Organizing the Information

Take time to introduce the importance of well-organized reports. Students will draw this conclusion themselves when they complete the following exercise.

1. Reproduce pages 7 and 8. Both reports include exactly the same sentences.
2. Give students page 7 and read the passage together. Then hand out page 8. Compare the unorganized writing and the organized writing.
   - Which piece is easier to read?
   - Which piece is easier to understand?
   - In which piece would it be easier to locate specific information?

A carefully developed note taker makes report organization simple. Each subtopic can be addressed in a paragraph with a main idea or topic sentence and other sentences (supporting sentences) that give more information about the idea. The *subtopic paragraphs* then become the report.

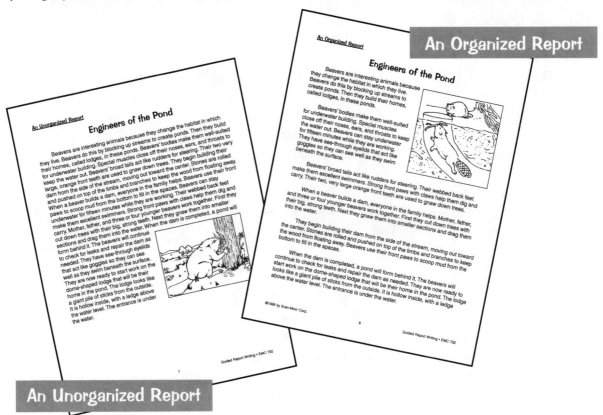

An Organized Report

An Unorganized Report

Engineers of the Pond

Beavers are interesting animals because they change the habitat in which they live. Beavers do this by blocking up streams to create ponds. Then they build their homes, called lodges, in these ponds. Beavers' bodies make them well-suited for underwater building. Special muscles close off their noses, ears, and throats to keep the water out. Beavers' broad tails act like rudders for steering. Their two very large, orange front teeth are used to gnaw down trees. They begin building their dam from the side of the stream, moving out toward the center. Stones are rolled and pushed on top of the limbs and branches to keep the wood from floating away. When a beaver builds a dam, everyone in the family helps. Beavers use their front paws to scoop mud from the bottom to fill in the spaces. Beavers can stay underwater for fifteen minutes while they are working. Their webbed back feet make them excellent swimmers. Strong front paws with claws help them dig and carry. Mother, father, and three or four younger beavers work together. First they cut down trees with their big, strong teeth. Next they gnaw them into smaller sections and drag them into the water. When the dam is completed, a pond will form behind it. The beavers will continue to check for leaks and repair the dam as needed. They have see-through eyelids that act like goggles so they can see well as they swim beneath the surface. They are now ready to start work on the dome-shaped lodge that will be their home in the pond. The lodge looks like a giant pile of sticks from the outside. It is hollow inside, with a ledge above the water level. The entrance is under the water.

Engineers of the Pond

Beavers are interesting animals because they change the habitat in which they live. Beavers do this by blocking up streams to create ponds. Then they build their homes, called lodges, in these ponds.

Beavers' bodies make them well-suited for underwater building. Special muscles close off their noses, ears, and throats to keep the water out. Beavers can stay underwater for fifteen minutes while they are working. They have see-through eyelids that act like goggles so they can see well as they swim beneath the surface.

Beavers' broad tails act like rudders for steering. Their webbed back feet make them excellent swimmers. Strong front paws with claws help them dig and carry. Their two, very large orange front teeth are used to gnaw down trees.

When a beaver builds a dam, everyone in the family helps. Mother, father, and three or four younger beavers work together. First they cut down trees with their big, strong teeth. Next they gnaw them into smaller sections and drag them into the water.

They begin building their dam from the side of the stream, moving out toward the center. Stones are rolled and pushed on top of the limbs and branches to keep the wood from floating away. Beavers use their front paws to scoop mud from the bottom to fill in the spaces.

When the dam is completed, a pond will form behind it. The beavers will continue to check for leaks and repair the dam as needed. They are now ready to start work on the dome-shaped lodge that will be their home in the pond. The lodge looks like a giant pile of sticks from the outside. It is hollow inside, with a ledge above the water level. The entrance is under the water.

Topic Sentences

A good topic sentence is essential for a good paragraph. Help students write topic sentences that are specific to the information on their note takers. Model and practice writing topic sentences with this topic sentence minilesson.

1. Reproduce page 10 as a transparency.
2. Read the notes with your students.
3. Brainstorm ways to express the information in the form of a sentence. Be sure to acknowledge that the main idea may be expressed in several different topic sentences.

Possible Topic Sentences

Parts of a Hand

The hand has five different parts that help it function.

The hand is made up of many different parts.

Different parts working together help my hand move and feel.

Ben Franklin's Achievements

Ben Franklin is noted for his research, his inventions, and his writing.

Ben Franklin wore many "different hats"—a scientist's hat, an author's hat, and an organizer's hat.

Ben Franklin was one man who could do it all.

Golden Eagle

The Golden Eagle is a majestic bird.

The Golden Eagle's appearance reflects its job and its home.

The Golden Eagle looks like a strong and powerful flyer.

Wolf

The wolf is a hearty eater.

A wolf eats all kinds of meat.

Imagine eating 20 pounds of fresh meat in a single meal!

Wright Brothers

The Wright brothers' first flight was not like an airplane flight today.

On a beach in North Carolina, a 12-second airplane flight changed history.

Two brothers worked together to fly a simple biplane.

Jelly Beans

Making a jelly bean is a complicated process.

The center of a jelly bean is made differently than the shell.

Water, cornstarch, sugar, and corn syrup go through seven steps to become a sweet treat.

4. When the discussion has been completed, let each student select one of the topic sentences suggested by the group and write a paragraph containing the information provided in the "details" list.

Writing Topic Sentences

Parts of a Hand
- 8 small bones
- ligaments to hold the bones together
- nerves that feel
- muscles to move
- blood

Appearance of the Golden Eagle
- large, heavy hooked bill
- strong, sharp claws (talons)
- brown with golden tints on head and neck
- wide wingspan
- majestic

How a Jelly Bean Is Made
- ingredients mixed—water, cornstarch, sugar, corn syrup
- flavorings added
- mixture cooled
- cool liquid poured into tiny molds
- steam bath and sugar shower after centers harden
- colored syrup poured over
- shell hardens and is polished

Ben Franklin's Achievements
- research on electricity
- invented lightning rod
- invented freestanding, woodburning stove
- organized U.S. postal system
- wrote *Poor Richard's Almanac*

Wright Brothers' First Flight
- Orville—pilot
- at Kitty Hawk, North Carolina, on a sandy beach
- lasted only 12 seconds
- simple biplane that looked like a giant box kite

Eating Habits of a Wolf
- eats fresh meat
- 20 pounds of meat at a single meal
- usually hunts big animals (deer, moose)
- smaller prey (rabbit, mouse)
- can fish

6 Responding, Revising, Editing

Students look at their first drafts, rereading with an eye for sense and readability. They rewrite and revise to refine the text. At this point students may work together to fine-tune the writing. Corrections to grammar and mechanics are made.

Use the Report Conference Form on page 13 to work with students in responding to their reports. Students can work together, reading and responding to each other's reports after the form's use has been modeled for them.

7 Producing the Final Copy

The final copy of a report is "published" in finished form. The report may be a traditional handwritten report including illustrations, charts, and a bibliography. The report may be prepared on the computer using drawing and word processing programs. The report might be a multimedia presentation. Determine the appropriate type of report. Then allow time for developing this "publication" and for sharing the information with others.

8 Including Additional Materials

Bibliography
A list of the sources used should be included with each report. This list is called a bibliography. Provide a clear format for reporting the vital information about each source. Reproduce page 12 as a model for writing different bibliography entries.

Other Additional Materials
Enhance the report with any of these informative features.

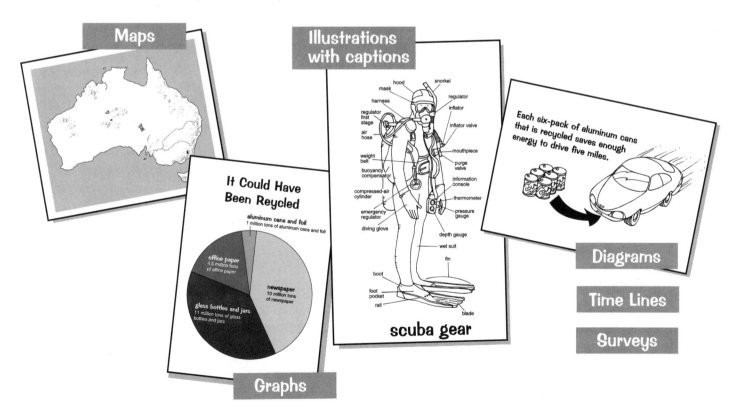

Maps

Illustrations with captions

It Could Have Been Recycled

aluminum cans and foil
1 million tons of aluminum cans and foil

office paper
4.5 million tons of office paper

newspaper
10 million tons of newspaper

glass bottles and jars
11 million tons of glass bottles and jars

scuba gear

hood
snorkel
mask
regulator
harness
inflator
regulator first stage
inflator valve
air hose
mouthpiece
weight belt
purge valve
buoyancy compensator
information console
compressed-air cylinder
thermometer
emergency regulator
pressure gauge
diving glove
depth gauge
wet suit
fin
boot
foot pocket
rail
blade

Each six-pack of aluminum cans that is recycled saves enough energy to drive five miles.

Diagrams

Time Lines

Surveys

Graphs

How to Write a Bibliography Entry

Book
Author (Last name, First name). <u>Title</u>. Place: Publisher, date.

For example:
Smith, John. <u>Native Americans</u>. New York: Best Books Press, 1995.

Encyclopedia
"Article title." <u>Encyclopedia</u>. Date.

For example:
"Lincoln, Abraham." <u>The New Children's Encyclopedia</u>. 1995.

Videotape
<u>Title</u>. Videotape. Production Company, date.

For example:
<u>Yellowstone National Park</u>. Videotape. Around Our Land Co., 1995.

CD-ROM
"Article title." CD-ROM. <u>CD-ROM Title</u>. Publisher, date.

For example:
"King, Martin Luther, Jr." CD-ROM. <u>The Best Electronic Encyclopedia</u>. Home Town Publishing, 1995.

Internet Source
Author. "Title." (Date) Name of site. URL

For example:
Carlon, Josh. "Happily Chewing." (July 1998) Big Bubble Gum. http://www.gum.com

Magazine Article
Author. "Name of article." <u>Magazine</u> (Date of publication): page numbers.

For example:
Sutter, Jeff. "The Secret of Good Coaching." <u>Everyday Athletes</u> (June 1990): pages 3–5.

Newspaper Article
Author, "Title," <u>Newspaper</u>, day month year.

For example:
Scoop, G. T., "Gas Prices Soar," <u>Evening Gazette</u>, 7 February 1999.

Note: For other types of information sources not listed here, devise your own citation format that provides needed facts.

Report Conference Form

Name: _____ **Date:** _____

Topic of Report:

Is the report well organized?   yes   no

Is the report easily understood?   yes   no

Does each paragraph have a topic sentence?   yes   no

Does each paragraph have supporting details that relate to the topic sentence?   yes   no

Strengths of Report _____

_____

_____

Things to Work On _____

_____

_____

Guided Report Writing • EMC 732

Report Conference Form

Name: _____ **Date:** _____

Topic of Report:

Is the report well organized?   yes   no

Is the report easily understood?   yes   no

Does each paragraph have a topic sentence?   yes   no

Does each paragraph have supporting details that relate to the topic sentence?   yes   no

Strengths of Report _____

_____

_____

Things to Work On _____

_____

_____

Chewing Gum

Advance Preparation

1. Reproduce the articles about chewing gum on pages 16–18. Include additional sources from the library and Internet if desired.

2. Reproduce the note taker on page 19 as a transparency or create a large chart on butcher paper.

1 Choosing a Topic

1. Define topic. **A topic is the subject of a report.**
2. Introduce chewing gum as the topic of this model report.

2 Formulating Subtopics

1. Define subtopics. **A subtopic is one part of a topic.**
2. Ask the class what kinds of things they want to know about chewing gum. Write their questions on the chalkboard or chart paper.
3. Guide the class in organizing their questions into several categories or subtopics. Suggested subtopics:
   History of Chewing Gum
   How Gum Is Made
   Why Gum Is Chewed
4. Write the subtopics on the note-taking transparency or chart.

3 Locating Information

1. Read the information on chewing gum: an encyclopedia article, an excerpt from a nonfiction book, and a pamphlet.
2. When your students are ready to include additional information sources, model locating information in an encyclopedia, reference or trade book, or on a bookmarked site on the Internet.
3. Remember to list the sources used so that the information will be available for the bibliography. (See sample entries on page 12.)

4 Taking Notes

1. Before reading a passage, ask students to listen for any information that pertains to the chosen subtopics.
2. Read a passage together, either aloud or silently. Start with a single paragraph to increase retention of information.
3. Have students identify information learned and the subtopic(s) to which it pertains.
4. Identify the key words that convey the information and write them on the note taker.
5. Reread the passage as necessary to address each subtopic.

5 Converting Notes to Paragraphs

1. Reread the notes on the chart.
2. Decide as a group which subtopic would make the best beginning point in reporting the information to someone else. There is more than one correct way to do this.
3. Formulate a main idea (topic) sentence to begin the writing. Write the sentence on a transparency or chart. If your students are not ready to do this, suggest a topic sentence they might use.
4. Add sentences that support the main idea using information from the note taker.
5. Repeat for each subtopic.

6 Responding, Revising, Editing

1. Proofread the finished product with the class.
   • Check first for sense and completeness.
   • Check for spelling, punctuation, and grammar.
2. Make corrections as needed.

7 Producing the Final Copy

1. Decide on a format—handwritten report, word-processed document, or multimedia presentation. (A report form is provided on page 21 if you wish to use it.)
2. Copy the report in the selected format.

8 Including Additional Materials

1. Prepare and add a bibliography.
2. Add charts, graphs, or maps.
3. Add illustrations and graphics.

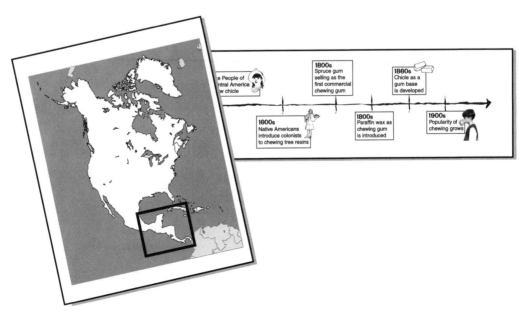

Chewing Gum

When you pop a piece of chewing gum into your mouth, do you ever wonder how people got the idea for chewing gum? Gum chewing began centuries ago. More than a thousand years ago the Mayan Indians of Mexico chewed chicle, the hardened juice of the sapodilla tree. The ancient Greeks made gum from the sap of the mastic tree. In North America, Native Americans in New England made gum from spruce sap. The early American colonists thought that the Native American chewing gum habit was silly, but soon they began to chew gum themselves.

The first shop to make and sell gum made from tree sap opened in the early 1800s. Soon the number of shops increased. Then an unusual event changed the chewing gum industry forever.

In 1860 Antonio López de Santa Anna, the Mexican general whose army defeated the Texans at the Alamo in 1836, came to New York to sell chicle as a type of rubber. A man named Thomas Adams tried to make things from this "rubber," but his experiment failed because the chicle would not harden. However, he discovered that the chicle could be chewed. He added flavorings and began to manufacture chewing gum. Before long, Adams was the rich owner of a large chewing gum factory.

Around the mid-1900s the main ingredient of chewing gum was chicle. Now synthetic gum bases made from melted rubber, waxes, or plastics are used. These warm, soft bases are strained for purification.

Softeners (to give the right amount of moisture, sweeteners, and flavorings) are added. After mixing, machines push out a thick ribbon of gum. The ribbon is flattened into a thin sheet. When the sheet cools, it is cut into pieces, wrapped, and packaged.

The United States produces about 24,000,000 miles of chewing gum each year! The retail sales of chewing gum are over $2 billion dollars a year. Surveys report that the average American chews 200 sticks of gum a year. The chewing gum industry has grown into a competitive business throughout the world.

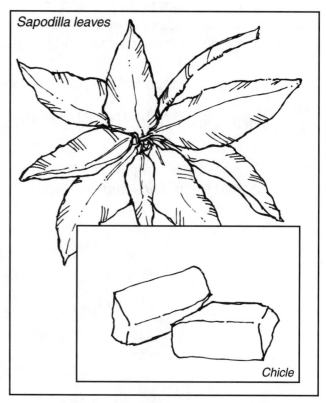

Sapodilla leaves

Chicle

Chicle is the sap produced by the sapodilla tree.

"Chewing Gum." Know-It-All Encyclopedia. 1999.

The History of Chewing Gum

For many centuries, the Mayans and other peoples of Central America chewed chicle. Chicle is the milky juice (latex) of the sapodilla tree. People in other lands chewed various resins, leaves, and grasses. Native Americans in New England taught the early colonists to chew spruce tree resins. Spruce gum was sold in the United States in the early 1800s as the first commercial chewing gum. Later, chewing gum made of paraffin wax was introduced.

In the 1860s the use of chicle as a chewing gum base was developed. Its resilient chewing quality and ability to hold flavors made it a favorite type of gum. Better-tasting gum, plus the development of modern processing, packaging, and promotional methods led to a rise in the popularity of chewing gum which began in the early 1900s.

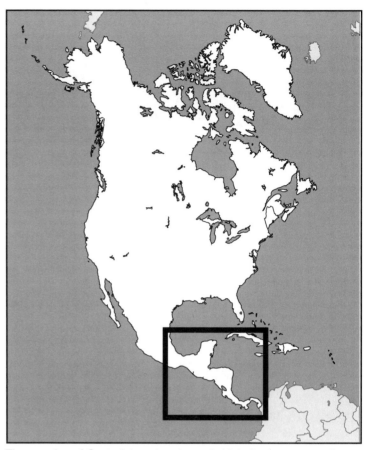

The peoples of Central America chewed chicle for many centuries.

Modern chewing gum consists of gum base, corn syrup, sugar, and flavoring. The latex products used in chewing gum base are obtained from trees. The trees are tapped with grooved cuts from which the latex flows into containers. The latex is then collected, boiled down, and molded into blocks. Man-made products with properties similar to latex have been developed for use in combination with the natural latex products to make gum bases. In the manufacturing process the gum-base ingredients are washed, ground, sterilized, and blended. The melted base is combined with corn syrup, sugar, and flavoring. The dough-like mixture is then rolled into sheets and divided into sticks. Essential oils from plants such as peppermint and spearmint provide the flavors.

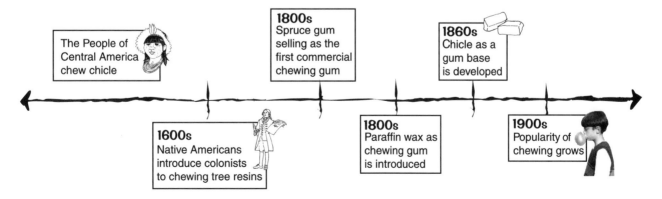

The People of Central America chew chicle

1600s
Native Americans introduce colonists to chewing tree resins

1800s
Spruce gum selling as the first commercial chewing gum

1800s
Paraffin wax as chewing gum is introduced

1860s
Chicle as a gum base is developed

1900s
Popularity of chewing grows

Incisor, Peter. <u>The History of Chewing Gum</u>. Anytown: Educational Publishers, 1990.

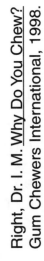

So whether you're looking for a sweet treat, concentrating on a hard job, or driving across the continental divide—chew it up!

Right, Dr. I. M. Why Do You Chew? Gum Chewers International, 1998.

---

fold forward

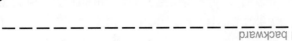

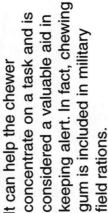
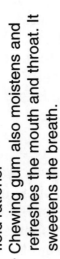

There are many different reasons why people chew gum.

- It's fun. The flavors are tasty and it provides a nonfat snack.
- Scientific studies at Columbia University report that chewing gum helps people relax. It reduces muscular tension and makes people feel at ease.
- It can help the chewer concentrate on a task and is considered a valuable aid in keeping alert. In fact, chewing gum is included in military field rations.
- Chewing gum also moistens and refreshes the mouth and throat. It sweetens the breath.
- After meals, chewing gum stimulates saliva that helps to neutralize traces of acids that may cause tooth decay.
- Chewing gum while driving over a mountain pass or taking off in an airplane can help relieve pressure in the ears.

---

fold backward

Why Do You Chew?
by Dr. I. M. Right

Chew it up, chew it up, Chewing Gum.
Chew it up, chew it up, Chewing Gum.

Open the package.
Pull out a stick.
Then unwrap it.
Pop it in quick.

Chew it up, chew it up, Chewing Gum.
Chew it up, chew it up, Chewing Gum.

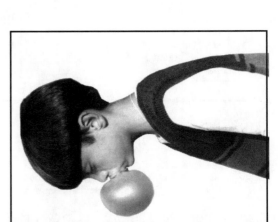

The Sticky Facts

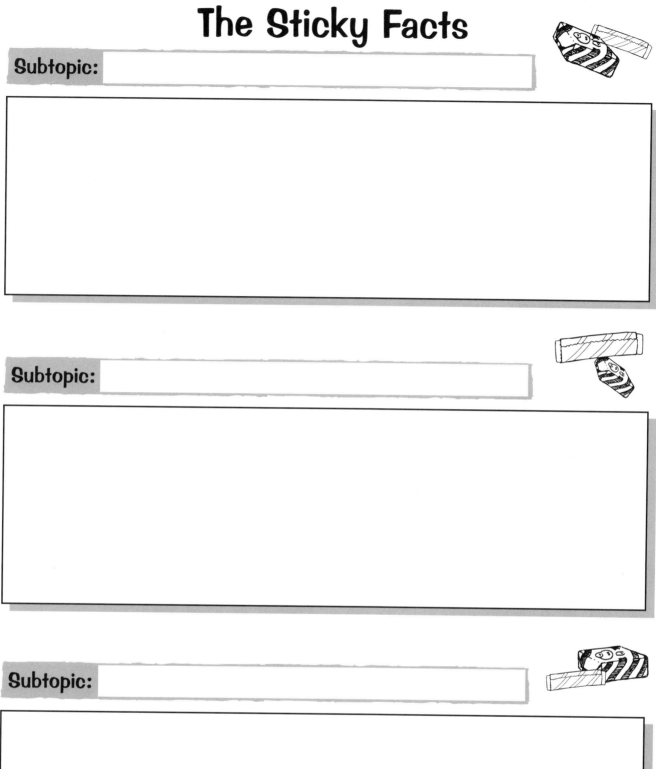

Subtopic:

Subtopic:

Subtopic:

Guided Report Writing • EMC 732

Chewing Gum Report Form

1. Copy the chewing gum report on the stick-of-gum pull-tab. Cut out the pull-tab.
2. Color and cut out the gum label.
3. Fold a piece of 9" x 12" (23 x 30.5 cm) paper in half to make a folder.
4. Insert the stick-of-gum pull-tab in the folder. Glue the folder closed as shown.
5. Glue the gum label to the front of the folder.

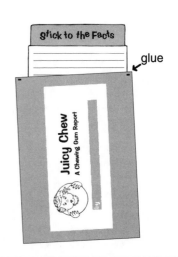

Juicy Chew
A Chewing Gum Report

by

Juicy Chew
A Chewing Gum Report

by

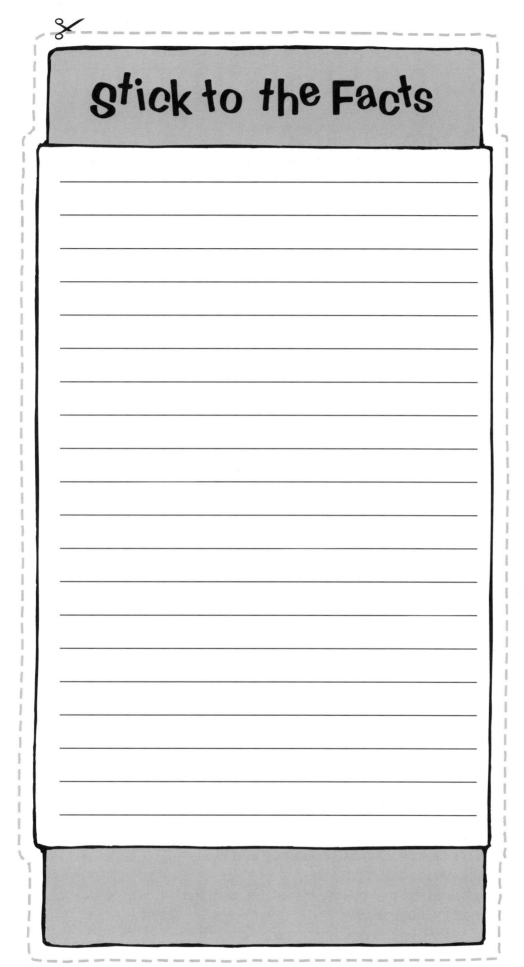

Stick to the Facts

Guided Report Writing • EMC 732

Guided Report 2
Christopher Columbus

Advance Preparation
1. Reproduce the information about Christopher Columbus on pages 24–28. Include additional sources from your library and the Internet if desired.
2. Reproduce the note taker on page 29 as a transparency or create a large chart on butcher paper.

1 Choosing a Topic

1. Define topic. **A topic is the subject of a report.**
2. Introduce Christopher Columbus as the topic of this model report.

2 Formulating Subtopics

1. Define subtopics. **A subtopic is one part of a topic.**
2. Ask the class what kinds of things they want to know about Christopher Columbus. Write their questions on the chalkboard or chart paper.
3. Guide the class in organizing their questions into several categories or subtopics. Suggested subtopics:
   Childhood
   Accomplishments
   Importance in History
4. Write the subtopics on the note-taking transparency or chart.

3 Locating Information

1. Read the information about Christopher Columbus: a book excerpt and a time line.
2. When your students are ready to include additional information sources, model locating information in an encyclopedia, reference or trade book, or on a bookmarked site on the Internet.
3. Remember to list the sources used so that the information will be available for the bibliography. (See sample entries on page 12.)

4 Taking Notes

1. Before reading a passage, ask students to listen for any information that pertains to the chosen subtopics.
2. Read a passage together, either aloud or silently. Start with a single paragraph to increase retention of information.
3. Have students identify information learned and the subtopic(s) to which it pertains.
4. Identify the key words that convey the information and write them on the note taker.
5. Reread the passage as necessary to address each subtopic.

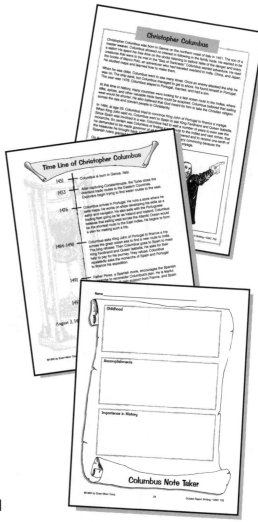

5 Converting Notes to Paragraphs

1. Reread the notes on the chart.
2. Decide as a group which subtopic would make the best beginning point in reporting the information to someone else. There is more than one correct way to do this. You might begin with Columbus's childhood if you were organizing the report in chronological order. However, you could also begin the report with a paragraph on the value of Columbus's "discovery" of the new world and then move to a discussion of his life.
3. Formulate a main idea (topic) sentence to begin the writing. Write the sentence on a transparency or chart. If your students are not ready to do this, suggest a topic sentence they might use.
4. Add sentences that support the main idea and include information from the note taker.
5. Repeat for each subtopic.

6 Responding, Revising, Editing

1. Proofread the finished product with the class.
   • Check first for sense and completeness.
   • Check for spelling, punctuation, and grammar.
2. Make corrections as needed.

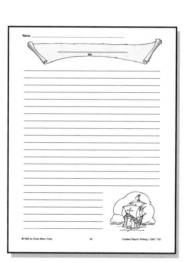

7 Producing the Final Copy

1. Decide on a format—handwritten report, word-processed document, or multimedia presentation. (A report form is provided on page 30 if you wish to use it.)
2. Copy the report in the selected format.

8 Including Additional Materials

1. Prepare and add a bibliography.
2. Add charts, graphs, or maps. Model the use of a map as a report add-on. Reproduce the map on page 29. Include the map with the final report.
3. Add illustrations and graphics.

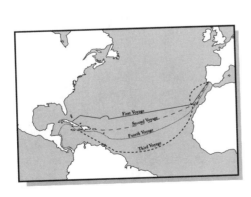

Christopher Columbus

Christopher Columbus was born in Genoa on the northern coast of Italy in 1451. The son of a master weaver, Columbus showed no interest in following in the family trade. He wanted to be a sailor! He spent his free time on the docks listening to sailors' tales of the danger and scary creatures that were to be met in the "Sea of Darkness." Columbus wanted adventure. He read the books of Marco Polo, an adventurer who had traveled overland to India, China, and Japan. He studied maps and learned how to make them.

When he was older, Columbus went to sea many times. Once an enemy attacked the ship he was on. The ship sank, but Columbus managed to get to shore. He found himself in Portugal. The year was 1476. Columbus stayed in Portugal, married, and had a son.

At this time in history, many countries were looking for a fast ocean route to the Indies, where silks, spices, and other valuable trade items could be acquired. Columbus believed that sailing west would be shorter. He also believed that God meant for him to take the Christian religion across the sea and convert people to Christianity.

In 1484, at age 33, Columbus tried to convince King John of Portugal to finance a voyage. When King John said no, Columbus went to Spain to ask King Ferdinand and Queen Isabella. Since Spain was involved in a war, Columbus had to wait a number of years to even see the monarchs. So certain was Columbus of finding a new route to the Indies and vast riches, that he demanded to be made governor of all the lands he discovered and to receive one-tenth of the treasures he brought back. Columbus must have been very convincing because the Spanish rulers granted him the necessary funds to make his voyage.

On August 3, 1492, the *Niña,* the *Pinta,* and the *Santa Maria* loaded with 100 men, cats to catch the ships' rats, food, water, weapons, and trinkets to trade sailed west into the open sea. Columbus expected to reach Japan in 2,400 miles. The sailors became angry and worried as it became obvious that they had sailed much farther than that and had not reached Japan. They begged him to turn back, and even threatened to mutiny, but Columbus was able to calm their fears and persuade them to go on.

On October 12, 1492, land was reached. Columbus named the land San Salvador and called the natives Indians. (He believed that he'd reached the East Indies.) Searching for gold, Columbus sailed from island to island. There were many curiosities—barkless dogs, brightly colored parrots, tobacco—but little gold. They landed on Cuba and on Haiti (which Columbus named Hispaniola).

Sailing along the coast of Haiti at night, the *Santa Maria* ran aground. The natives they encountered had gold. Columbus was excited. This was what they'd been searching for! He left 39 men in Hispaniola to build a fort. He sailed back to Spain for more ships to carry all the gold that would be collected by the time he returned.

On his second voyage from Spain, Columbus had seventeen ships, which carried many men to settle Hispaniola and collect gold. Arriving in Hispaniola, he found that things had gone badly in his absence. The men were dead and the fort was destroyed. Things went badly for the new settlers too. There was much sickness, and collecting the gold was very difficult.

In 1496 Columbus again returned to Spain to attempt to explain to Ferdinand and Isabella what had gone wrong. Luckily for Columbus, the king and queen were willing to give him another chance. This time he was sent farther south in an attempt to find gold. On this voyage, Columbus landed on an island off the coast of South America which he named Trinidad.

Arriving next in Hispaniola, Columbus discovered that the settlers were very unhappy. In fact, they complained so loudly to Spain that Ferdinand and Isabella sent a special representative to find out what was going on. The representative arrested Columbus and sent him back to Spain in chains.

Amazingly enough, the king and queen were willing to give Columbus one final chance. In 1502 he set sail for India again. This time he sailed up and down the coast of Central America, finding unfriendly natives and no gold. He lost two of his four ships and had to run the last two ashore on Jamaica because they were falling apart. Stranded on Jamaica for one year, Columbus did not get back to Spain until November 1504.

Columbus died May 20, 1506, still insisting he'd found the Indies. He hadn't, of course, but his four voyages started a wave of exploration which changed the course of world history.

History, Professor Harvey. <u>Christopher Columbus</u>. Researchville: History Press, 1989.

Time Line of Christopher Columbus

1451 — Columbus is born in Genoa, Italy.

1453 — After capturing Constantinople, the Turks close the overland trade routes to the Eastern Countries. Explorers begin trying to find water routes to the east.

1476 — Columbus arrives in Portugal. He runs a store where he sells maps. He works on ships developing his skills as a sailor and navigator. He also sails with the Portuguese trading fleet going as far as Ireland and Iceland. Columbus believes that sailing west across the Atlantic Ocean would be the shortest route to the East Indies. He begins to form a plan for making such a trip.

1484–1490 — Columbus asks King John of Portugal to finance a trip across the great ocean sea to find a new route to India. The king refuses. Then Columbus goes to Spain to meet King Ferdinand and Queen Isabella. He asks for their help to pay for his journey. They refuse. Columbus repeatedly asks the monarchs of Spain and Portugal to finance his expedition.

1491 — Father Perez, a Spanish monk, encourages the Spanish monarchs to reconsider Columbus's plan. He is fearful that Columbus will gain support from France, and Spain would be the loser.

1492 — The War with the Moors ends. Queen Isabella and King Ferdinand decide to give Columbus what he has asked for.

August 3, 1492 — Columbus sets sail with three ships on his first voyage across the Atlantic. Columbus is sure he will soon prove that there was a direct western route from Europe to the East Indies.

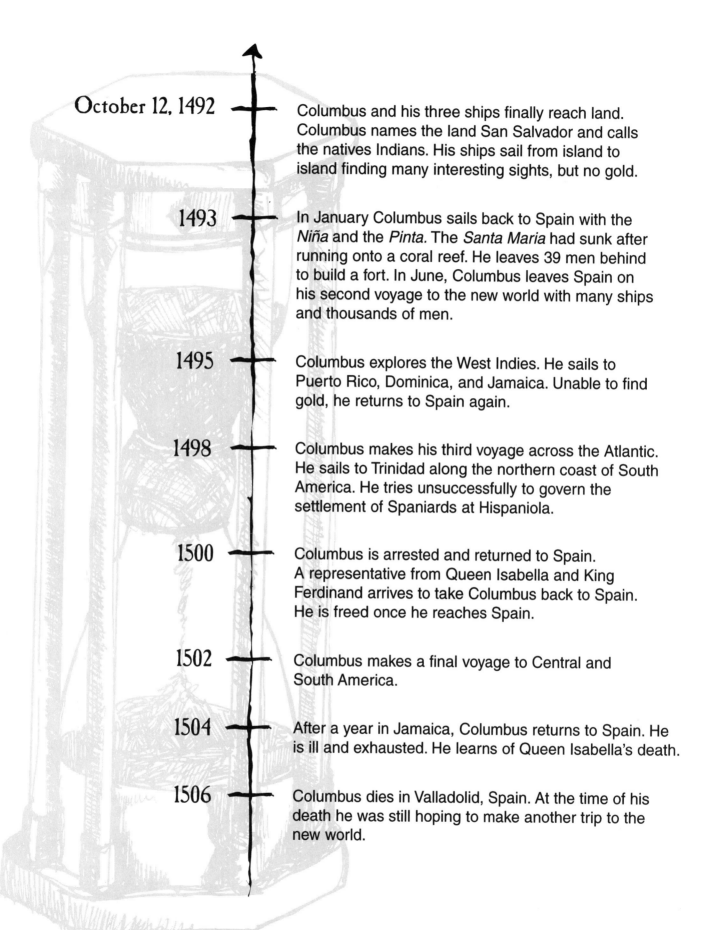

October 12, 1492 — Columbus and his three ships finally reach land. Columbus names the land San Salvador and calls the natives Indians. His ships sail from island to island finding many interesting sights, but no gold.

1493 — In January Columbus sails back to Spain with the *Niña* and the *Pinta.* The *Santa Maria* had sunk after running onto a coral reef. He leaves 39 men behind to build a fort. In June, Columbus leaves Spain on his second voyage to the new world with many ships and thousands of men.

1495 — Columbus explores the West Indies. He sails to Puerto Rico, Dominica, and Jamaica. Unable to find gold, he returns to Spain again.

1498 — Columbus makes his third voyage across the Atlantic. He sails to Trinidad along the northern coast of South America. He tries unsuccessfully to govern the settlement of Spaniards at Hispaniola.

1500 — Columbus is arrested and returned to Spain. A representative from Queen Isabella and King Ferdinand arrives to take Columbus back to Spain. He is freed once he reaches Spain.

1502 — Columbus makes a final voyage to Central and South America.

1504 — After a year in Jamaica, Columbus returns to Spain. He is ill and exhausted. He learns of Queen Isabella's death.

1506 — Columbus dies in Valladolid, Spain. At the time of his death he was still hoping to make another trip to the new world.

History, I. C. <u>Christopher Columbus: A Time Line</u>. San Francisco: Learning Inc., 1986.

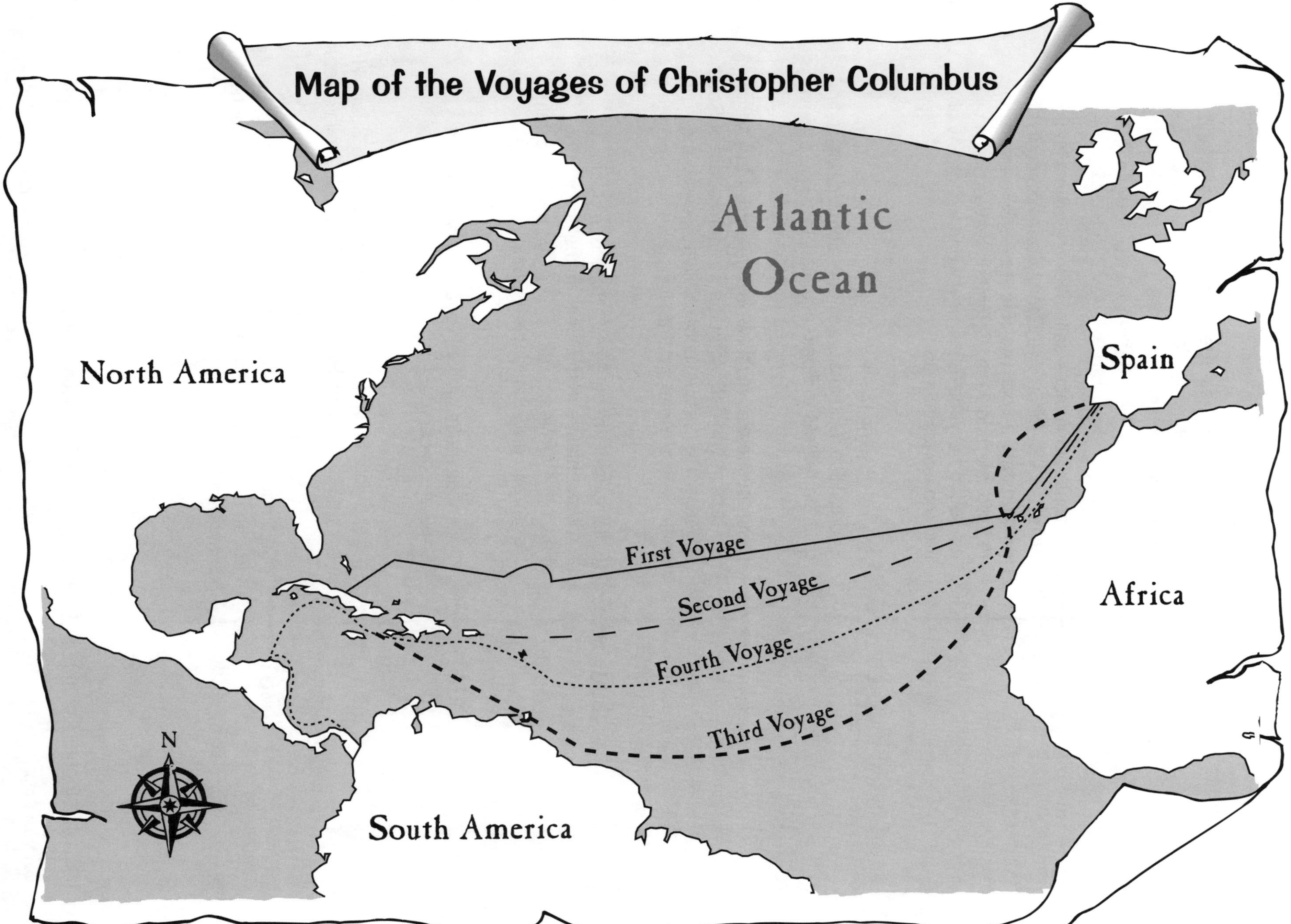

Map of the Voyages of Christopher Columbus

Spain

Africa

Atlantic Ocean

First Voyage

Second Voyage

Fourth Voyage

Third Voyage

North America

South America

N

"Map of the Voyages of Christopher Columbus." Extra Atlas. 1990.

©1999 by Evan-Moor Corp.

Childhood

Accomplishments

Importance in History

Columbus Note Taker

 Guided Report Writing • EMC 732

Name _____

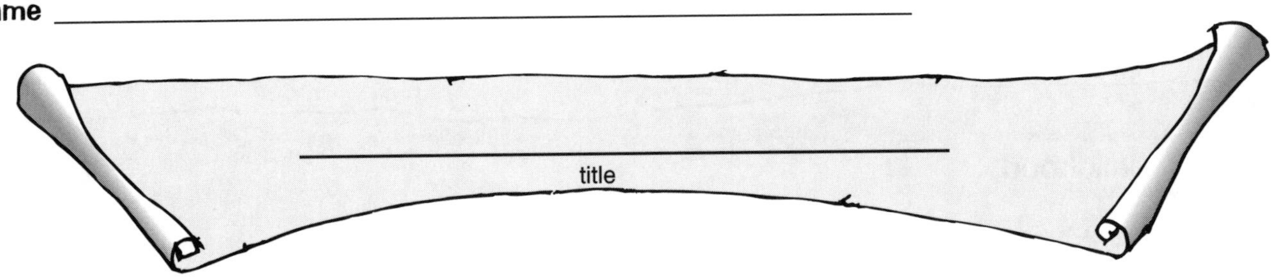

_____
title

_____
_____
_____
_____
_____
_____
_____
_____
_____
_____
_____
_____
_____
_____
_____
_____
_____
_____
_____
_____
_____
_____

Guided Report 3

The Moon

1 Choosing a Topic

1. Define topic. **A topic is the subject of a report.**
2. Introduce the Moon as the topic of this model report.

2 Formulating Subtopics

1. Define subtopics. **A subtopic is one part of a topic.**
2. Ask the class what kinds of things they want to know about the Moon. Write their questions on the chalkboard or chart paper.
3. Guide the class in organizing their questions into several categories or subtopics.
   Suggested subtopics:
   - What the Moon Is Like
   - Phases of the Moon
   - Where the Moon Is
4. Write the subtopics on the note-taking transparency or chart.

3 Locating Information

1. Read the information about the Moon:
   a textbook entry and a science experiment. Do the science experiment together as a class or assign it for homework.
2. When your students are ready to include additional information sources, model locating information in an encyclopedia, reference or trade book, or on a bookmarked site on the Internet.
3. Remember to list the sources used so that the information will be available for the bibliography.

4 Taking Notes

1. Before reading a passage, ask students to listen for any information that pertains to the chosen subtopics.
2. Read a passage together, either aloud or silently. Start with a single paragraph to increase retention of information.
3. Have students identify information learned and the subtopic(s) to which it pertains.
4. Identify the key words that convey the information and write them on the note taker.
5. Reread the passage as necessary to address each subtopic.

Advance Preparation

1. Reproduce the information about the Moon on pages 33–36. Include additional sources from your library and the Internet if desired.
2. Reproduce the note taker on page 37 as a transparency or create a large chart on butcher paper.

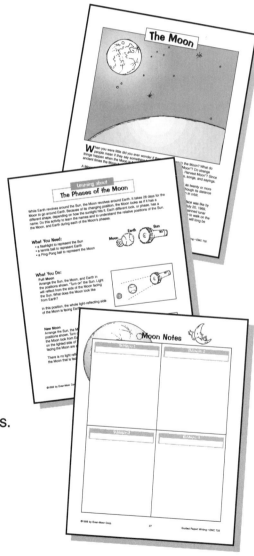

5 Converting Notes to Paragraphs

1. Reread the notes on the chart.
2. Decide as a group which subtopic would make the best beginning point in reporting the information to someone else. There is more than one correct way to do this.
3. Formulate a main idea (topic) sentence to begin the writing. Write the sentence on a transparency or chart. If your students are not ready to do this, suggest a topic sentence they might use.
4. Add sentences that support the main idea using information from the note taker.
5. Repeat for each subtopic.

6 Responding, Revising, Editing

1. Proofread the finished product with the class.
   • Check first for sense and completeness.
   • Check for spelling, punctuation, and grammar.
2. Make corrections as needed.

7 Producing the Final Copy

1. Decide on a format—handwritten report, word-processed document, or multimedia presentation. (A report form is provided on page 38 if you wish to use it.)
2. Copy the report in the selected format.

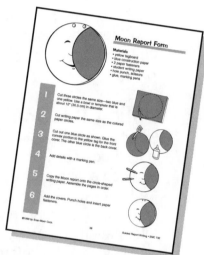

8 Including Additional Materials

1. Prepare and add a bibliography.
2. Add charts, graphs, or maps.
3. Add illustrations and graphics.

Phases of the Moon

The Moon

When you were little did you ever wonder if there was a man in the Moon? What do people mean if they say something happens "once in a blue Moon"? Do strange things happen when the Moon is full? Have you ever sung "Shine on, Harvest Moon"? Since ancient times the Moon has been the subject of many legends, poems, songs, and sayings.

A Moon is any object that circles a planet. Some planets have as many as twenty or more moons. Earth has just one. Our Moon is closer to us than any planet, although its distance is almost ten times Earth's circumference. Earth's gravity keeps the Moon in orbit.

For many years scientists could only speculate about what the Moon's surface was like by viewing it through telescopes or examining satellite photographs. Then on July 20, 1969, the world thrilled to the words "Houston...The Eagle has landed." The first manned lunar landing had been successful. Astronaut Neil Armstrong became the first man to walk on the Moon. His words, "That's one small step for man, one giant leap for mankind," will long be remembered.

The surface of the Moon is rocky, barren, grayish, and covered with a layer of fine dust. There are flat areas, craters, and high mountains, many of which are dead volcanoes. Some craters are less than one foot (30 centimeters) across; others are large enough to be seen from Earth and are as much as 700 miles (1,100 kilometers) across. Meteorites crashing into the Moon's surface millions of years ago probably made these craters.

Earth is roughly four times the size of the Moon. Earth is also 81 times heavier than the Moon. Because the Moon weighs so much less than Earth, its gravity is much less than Earth's. You would weigh 1/6 of your Earth weight on the Moon. If you weigh 90 pounds on Earth, you will weigh only 15 pounds on the Moon. Just think how high you could jump! In fact, astronauts who have landed on the Moon have had fun being "lightweights." One astronaut, Alan B. Shepard, Jr., demonstrated that a golf ball could be hit six times farther on the Moon.

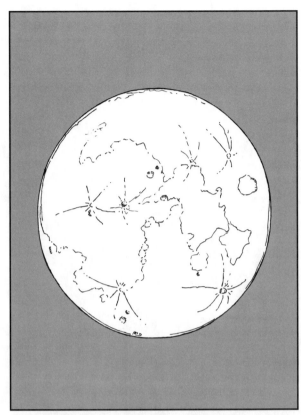

The surface of the Moon is rocky, barren, grayish, and covered with a layer of fine dust.

Many of the differences between Earth and the Moon are caused by the lack of atmosphere on the Moon. Since there is no air, sound cannot travel. Your parents would never complain about your music being too loud, but you wouldn't hear it either! Footprints left on the Moon's surface will be there forever because there is no wind. With no atmosphere to deflect sunlight, the Moon's sky is black. Also, the Sun's heat is extremely intense. A day on the Moon lasts 14 days; temperatures climb above the boiling point of water. The 14-day-long nights are very, very cold.

From Earth only one side of the Moon is visible because the Moon takes the same amount of time to turn on its axis as it does to go around Earth. No one ever saw the "dark side" of the Moon until the 1960s when orbiting spacecraft sent back photographs.

Crater, Rocky. "The Moon." <u>In Elementary Science</u>. New York: Learning, Inc., 1997.

Learning about

The Phases of the Moon

While Earth revolves around the Sun, the Moon revolves around Earth. It takes 28 days for the Moon to go around Earth. Because of its changing position, the Moon looks as if it has a different shape, depending on how the sunlight hits it. Each different look, or phase, has a name. Do this activity to learn the names and to understand the relative positions of the Sun, the Moon, and Earth during each of the Moon's phases.

What You Need:

- a flashlight to represent the Sun
- a tennis ball to represent Earth
- a Ping-Pong ball to represent the Moon

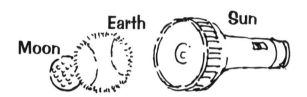

What You Do:

Full Moon

Arrange the Sun, the Moon, and Earth in the positions shown. "Turn on" the Sun. Light will reflect from the side of the Moon facing the Sun. What does the Moon look like from Earth?

In this position, the whole light-reflecting side of the Moon is facing Earth.

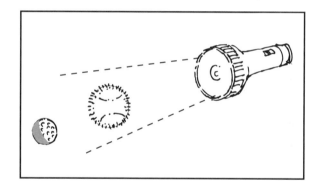

New Moon

Arrange the Sun, the Moon, and Earth in the positions shown. Turn on the Sun. How will the Moon look from Earth now? It is daytime on the lighted side of Earth, so the people facing the Moon are also facing the Sun.

There is no light reflecting from the side of the Moon that is facing the people on Earth.

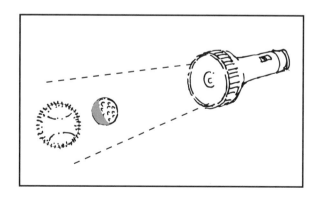

Last Quarter Moon

Arrange the Sun, the Moon, and Earth in the positions shown. Turn on the Sun. From Earth the left side of the Moon will appear to be lit up, but the right side will be dark. What will that look like?

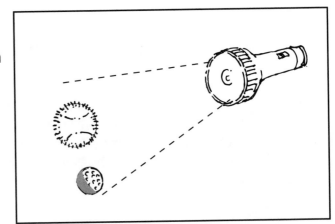

Crescent Moon

Arrange the Sun, the Moon, and Earth in the positions shown. Only a sliver of the light-reflecting side of the Moon is visible from Earth.

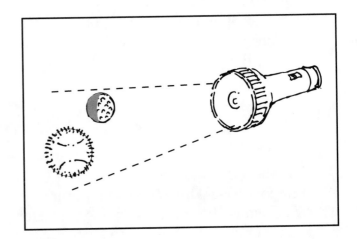

Gibbous Moon

Arrange the Sun, the Moon, and Earth in the positions shown. Most of the light-reflecting side of the Moon is visible.

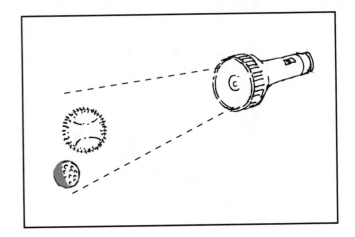

Hands-On, Lotta. <u>Learning by Doing</u>. Boston: Space Books Today, 1999.

Moon Notes

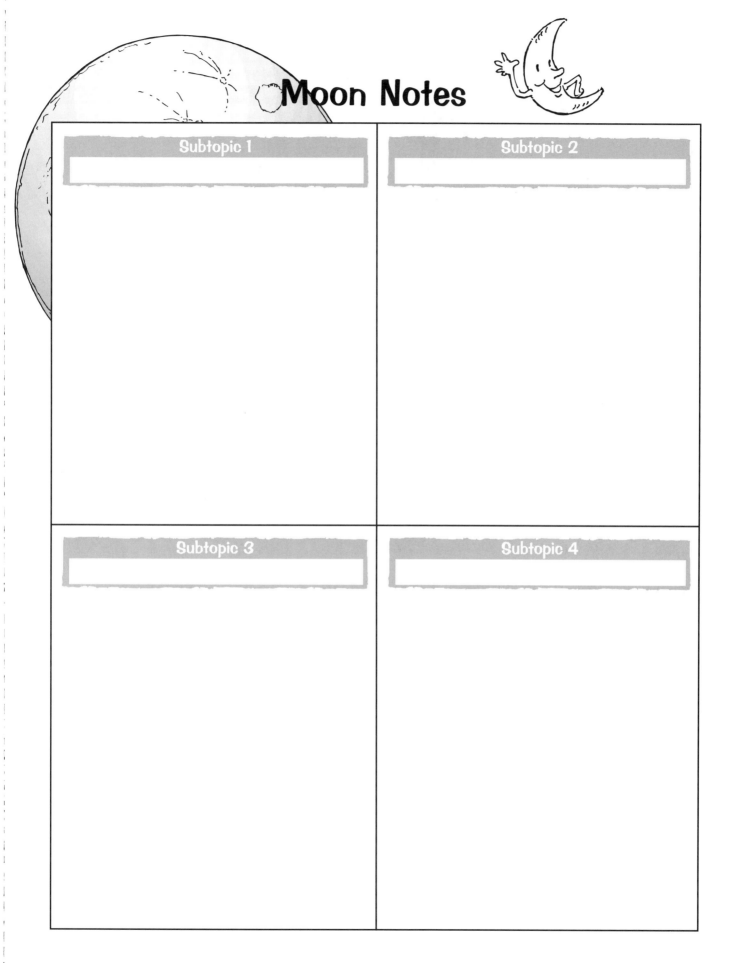

Subtopic 1	Subtopic 2

Subtopic 3	Subtopic 4

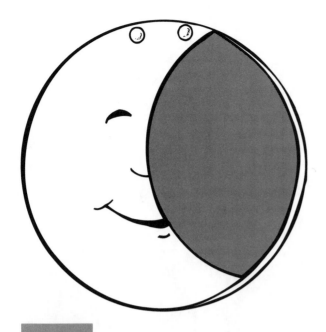

Moon Report Form

Materials
- yellow tagboard
- blue construction paper
- 2 paper fasteners
- student writing paper
- hole punch, scissors
- glue, marking pens

1 Cut three circles the same size—two blue and one yellow. Use a bowl or template that is about 12" (30.5 cm) in diameter.

2 Cut writing paper the same size as the colored paper circles.

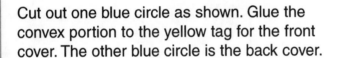

3 Cut out one blue circle as shown. Glue the convex portion to the yellow tag for the front cover. The other blue circle is the back cover.

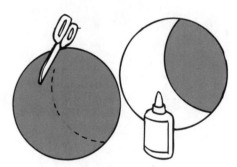

4 Add details with a marking pen.

5 Copy the Moon report onto the circle-shaped writing paper. Assemble the pages in order.

6 Add the covers. Punch holes and insert paper fasteners.

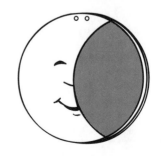

Guided Report 4
Koalas

Advance Preparation

1. Reproduce the information about koalas on pages 41–43. Include additional sources from your library and the Internet if desired.
2. Reproduce the note taker pocket on page 44 and provide four note cards for each student.

1 Choosing a Topic

1. Define topic. **A topic is the subject of a report.**
2. Introduce koalas as the topic of this model report.

2 Formulating Subtopics

1. Define subtopics. **A subtopic is one part of a topic.**
2. Ask the class what kinds of things they want to know about koalas. Write their questions on the chalkboard or chart paper.
3. Guide the class in organizing their questions into several categories or subtopics.

    Suggested subtopics:
    Appearance
    Eating Habits
    Habitat
    Enemies

4. Write the subtopics on the note cards or the chart.

3 Locating Information

1. Read the information about koalas: a magazine article and a sign at the zoo.
2. When your students are ready to include additional information sources, model locating information in an encyclopedia, reference or trade book, or on a bookmarked site on the Internet.
3. Remember to list any sources used so that the information will be available for the bibliography. (See sample entries on page 12.)

4 Taking Notes

1. Before reading a passage, ask students to listen for any information that pertains to the chosen subtopics.
2. Read a passage together, either aloud or silently. Start with a single paragraph to increase retention of information.
3. Have students identify information learned and the subtopic(s) to which it pertains.
4. Identify the key words that convey the information and write them on the note taker.
5. Reread the passage as necessary to address each subtopic.

koala pocket for note cards, page 44

5 Converting Notes to Paragraphs

1. Reread the notes.
2. Decide as a group which subtopic would make the best beginning point in reporting the information to someone else. There is more than one correct way to do this.
3. Formulate a main idea (topic) sentence to begin the writing. Write the sentence on a transparency or chart. If your students are not ready to do this, suggest a topic sentence they might use.
4. Add sentences that support the main idea using information from the note taker.
5. Repeat for each subtopic.

6 Responding, Revising, Editing

1. Proofread the finished product with the class.
   • Check first for sense and completeness.
   • Check for spelling, punctuation, and grammar.
2. Make corrections as needed.

7 Producing the Final Copy

1. Decide on a format—handwritten report, word-processed document, or multimedia presentation. (A report form is provided on page 45 if you wish to use it.)
2. Copy the report in the selected format.

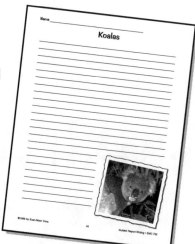

8 Including Additional Materials

1. Prepare and add a bibliography.
2. Add charts, graphs, or maps.
3. Add illustrations and graphics.

Koalas

What looks like a cuddly teddy bear, lives in trees, has thick woolly fur, a big black nose, rounded furry ears, and doesn't drink water?

It's the adorable koala.

Although they resemble bears, koalas are not bears, they are marsupials. The word "marsupial" comes from the Latin word *marsupium,* meaning pouch. A koala, therefore, is related to kangaroos, opossums, and wombats. The name koala comes from an aboriginal word meaning "no water" or "no drink." Koalas are found in coastal areas of northeast and southern Australia. The northern koalas are somewhat smaller and have fur that is shorter and less thick due to the hotter weather in the north. Koalas live in eucalyptus forests.

Eucalyptus trees are living room, bedroom, and kitchen to the koala. Because they spend most of their lives in trees, koalas are called "arboreal" animals. Koalas eat two and one-half pounds of eucalyptus leaves daily. The water in the leaves is all the koala needs. They may also eat eucalyptus shoots, bark, and flowers. The oil in the leaves gives the koalas a strong odor, something like a cough drop. At a certain time of the year the leaves of one type of eucalyptus are poisonous. The koala's keen sense of smell can detect this change and the animal moves to another kind of eucalyptus tree. When a koala has eaten most of the leaves on a tree, it may jump to another nearby tree, or it may move on the ground. Koalas are not graceful on the ground, but if chased they can run as fast as a man. Koalas feed at night and may wander as far as two kilometers in search of food.

During the day koalas sleep in the treetops, often using a tree fork to support themselves.

A koala may sleep as many as twenty hours a day. During the winter they may go for days without moving or eating.

Such an unusual life calls for some special adaptations. The koala is well-suited to life in the trees. The koala is a remarkable climber. The toes on its feet separate into two sections. These opposing toes and razor-sharp claws enable the koala to grip branches securely. When climbing, the koala holds and pulls with its forelegs and pushes with its rear legs. The rear legs can also hold onto the trunk, freeing the forelegs for other activities.

When climbing, the koala holds and pulls with its forelegs and pushes with its rear legs.

A koala does not have a tail. Its rump has a thick layer of fur and fat—what a great cushion for sitting in a tree all day!

Like all marsupials, baby koalas spend time in their mothers' pouches. Born blind, deaf, and hairless, the bean-size babies use their senses of smell to find the pouches. They attach themselves to one of the mother's two teats or nipples. For about six months the baby will live in the pouch, growing fur, strong legs, and claws. Then the baby climbs onto the mother's back and spends the next few months riding. At about one year the baby koala is ready to leave the mother and take care of itself.

Koalas are now protected by law. They were almost wiped out by humans who hunted them for their fur. Many preserves have been set up in Australia to ensure that people will be able to see the charming koala for years to come.

Patient, U. R. "Koalas." Children's Digest (July 1995): pages 9–10.

The Koala

The koala is a mammal that lives in Australia. It has thick fur to keep it warm and dry. Its baby is born live and is fed milk from the mother's body. In all of these ways a koala is like other mammals. But a koala is a special kind of mammal called a marsupial. A female marsupial has a pouch on her underside. This is where she carries her baby as it grows.

When a koala baby is born, it is blind and has no hair. The baby is only about the size of a lima bean. This tiny baby must crawl up into its mother's pouch. There it will eat, sleep, and grow. Even after it is able to come out of the pouch, it will hop back in when it is scared or sleepy. The young koala rides on its mother's back until it can take care of itself.

A koala eats the leaves of eucalyptus (gum) trees. It eats the tender shoots that grow on the tips of the branches. A koala has two sharp teeth in front for tearing leaves or stripping bark. It has flat teeth in back for chewing the leaves. A koala may go on the ground to move to a new tree.

A koala does sometimes drink, but the leaves that it eats provide most of the water it needs.

The koala is a nocturnal animal. This means that it is more active at night than during the day. A koala doesn't have a home or a nest. It just wedges its body into the fork of a tree. It wraps its arms or legs around a branch, closes its eyes, and goes to sleep.

Information Posted at Happy Zoo. 1999.

Guided Report Writing • EMC 732

Name _____

Fold on the dotted line to make a pocket to hold your koala note cards.

Name _____

Koalas

_____

_____

_____

_____

_____

_____

_____

_____

_____

_____

_____

_____

_____

_____

_____

_____

_____

_____

Guided Report 5
Jane Goodall

Advance Preparation

1. Reproduce the information about Jane Goodall on pages 48–51. Include additional sources from your library and the Internet if desired.

2. Reproduce the note taker on page 52 as a transparency or create a large chart on butcher paper.

1 Choosing a Topic

1. Define topic. **A topic is the subject of a report.**
2. Introduce Jane Goodall as the topic of this model report.

2 Formulating Subtopics

1. Define subtopics. **A subtopic is one part of a topic.**
2. Ask the class what kinds of things they want to know about Jane Goodall. Write their questions on the chalkboard or chart paper.
3. Guide the class in organizing their questions into several categories or subtopics.
   Suggested subtopics:
      Childhood
      Accomplishments
      Importance in History
4. Write the subtopics on the note-taking transparency or chart.

3 Locating Information

1. Read the information about Jane Goodall: a biography, a poster, and a news release.
2. When your students are ready to include additional information sources, model locating information in an encyclopedia, reference or trade book, or on a bookmarked site on the Internet.
3. Remember to list the sources used so that the information will be available for the bibliography. (See sample entries on page 12.)

4 Taking Notes

1. Before reading a passage, ask students to listen for any information that pertains to the chosen subtopics.
2. Read a passage together, either aloud or silently. Start with a single paragraph to increase retention of information.
3. Have students identify information learned and the subtopic(s) to which it pertains.
4. Identify the key words that convey the information and write them on the note taker.
5. Reread the passage as necessary to address each subtopic.

5 Converting Notes to Paragraphs

1. Reread the notes on the chart.
2. Decide as a group which subtopic would make the best beginning point in reporting the information to someone else. There is more than one correct way to do this. You might begin with Goodall's childhood if you were organizing the report in chronological order. However, you could also begin the report with a paragraph on the importance of Goodall's study of the chimpanzees and then move to a discussion of her childhood.
3. Formulate a main idea (topic) sentence to begin the writing. Write the sentence on a transparency or chart. If your students are not ready to do this, suggest a topic sentence they might use.
4. Add sentences that support the main idea and include information from the note taker.
5. Repeat for each subtopic.

6 Responding, Revising, Editing

1. Proofread the finished product with the class.
   - Check first for sense and completeness.
   - Check for spelling, punctuation, and grammar.
2. Make corrections as needed.

7 Producing the Final Copy

1. Decide on a format—handwritten report, word-processed document, or multimedia presentation. (A report form is provided on page 53 if you wish to use it.)
2. Copy the report in the selected format.

8 Including Additional Materials

1. Prepare and add a bibliography.
2. Add charts, graphs, or maps.
3. Add illustrations and graphics.

Jane Goodall

Jane Goodall

Jane Goodall was born in England on April 3, 1934. As a child in the seaside town of Bournemouth, Jane learned to love and appreciate nature. Jane liked to watch animals and take notes on their habits. Her favorite reading matter was Rudyard Kipling's animal stories and the Tarzan stories. She wrote a weekly newspaper about animals, called "The Alligator," which her mother typed for Jane and her friends. Jane disliked school and was frequently late. She preferred being outdoors watching animals. Jane did better after her mother convinced her that she needed to get good grades to become a scientist and go to Africa.

Although Jane wanted to attend a university, her mother could not afford to send her, so she went to secretarial school. After this schooling, Jane worked for a London movie company for three years. Jane's opportunity to go to Africa came when a school friend who lived on a farm in Kenya invited her to come for a visit. To save money for her trip, Jane moved back home and worked in a restaurant.

In 1957, at the age of 23, Jane left England for Kenya, Africa. Although she enjoyed living on her friend's farm, she still wanted the opportunity to study wild animals. Jane went to see Dr. Louis Leakey, a famous scientist who studied ancient man. She got a job as his secretary at the National Museum of Natural History of Kenya. Here Jane learned anthropology and paleontology and worked with Dr. Leakey on digs searching for fossils and bones.

Dr. Leakey suggested that Jane go to Lake Tanganyika in Tanzania to study the chimpanzees that lived there. The Wilke Foundation agreed to pay for six months of expenses. Jane's mother went with her because the government wouldn't let her go into the jungle alone. Camp was set up in Gombe, the chimpanzee area. Jane had much to learn about the jungle. There were numerous hardships and dangers—insect bites, malaria, poisonous snakes, and fierce animals.

Gradually the chimps came to accept her presence. She gave them names—Flo, Fifi, and Goliath. Jane observed behaviors that humans had not recorded before. She saw chimps eat meat, use twigs to pull termites out of mounds, and sop up water with leaves.

From 1961 to 1967, Jane spent each winter at Cambridge University in England studying for a doctorate degree in animal behavior. Summers were spent with the chimps in Africa. During this time she married Baron Hugo Van Lawick. He was a photographer who had filmed her work for the National Geographic Society.

In 1965 a permanent research center was established at Gombe. The chimpanzee area was made a national park.

Jane's son was born in 1967. She nicknamed him "Grub," which means bush baby in Swahili. Jane and her family traveled throughout Africa, filming and writing about lions, cheetahs, and hyenas. She wrote books based on her notes from Gombe. She also wrote a book about her son growing up in Africa.

Today Jane Goodall continues her studies of wild animals in Africa. She also travels around the world promoting habitat preservation and animal rights.

Learning, Dr. Moore. "Jane Goodall." Boston: Famous People Publishers, 1995.

"Chimpanzees have given me so much. The long hours spent with them in the forest have enriched my life beyond measure. What I have learned from them has shaped my understanding of human behavior; of our place in nature."

Jane Goodall

When Jane Goodall was a baby in England, she slept with a stuffed toy chimpanzee. She always loved nature and animals. She was two when she hid earthworms under her pillow so that she could watch them at night. At four she stayed in a hen house for five hours as she waited for a hen to lay an egg.

In 1960 she used that same curiosity and perseverance when she began watching the chimpanzees on Tanzania's Gombe Stream Reserve. Patiently she waited and watched until the chimps accepted her. She gave each of the chimpanzees names and watched as generations grew up. Her careful notes and observations have helped scientists around the world understand animal behavior.

She formed the Jane Goodall Institute and today she travels around the world promoting animal rights and research.

Jane Goodall. Illustration by Art Sample. The Poster Gallery, 1999.

Jane Goodall Institute: Dedicated to Wildlife Research

By R. E. Search
Tribune Staff Writer

The Jane Goodall Institute, based in Ridgefield, Connecticut, is a nonprofit organization committed to wildlife research, environmental education, and the conservation and welfare of animals. The Institute is especially dedicated to researching and publicizing the unique needs of chimpanzees. One of the goals of the Institute is the long-term preservation of chimpanzees living in the wild. Founded in 1977 by Dr. Jane Goodall, the Institute continues to teach people around the world.

R. E. Search, "Jane Goodall Institute," Tribune, 9 September 1997.

Jane Goodall Institute: Dedicated to Wildlife Research

By R. E. Search
Tribune Staff Writer

The Jane Goodall Institute, based in Ridgefield, Connecticut, is a nonprofit organization committed to wildlife research, environmental education, and the conservation and welfare of animals. The Institute is especially dedicated to researching and publicizing the unique needs of chimpanzees. One of the goals of the Institute is the long-term preservation of chimpanzees living in the wild. Founded in 1977 by Dr. Jane Goodall, the Institute continues to teach people around the world.

R. E. Search, "Jane Goodall Institute," Tribune, 9 September 1997.

Jane Goodall Institute: Dedicated to Wildlife Research

By R. E. Search
Tribune Staff Writer

The Jane Goodall Institute, based in Ridgefield, Connecticut, is a nonprofit organization committed to wildlife research, environmental education, and the conservation and welfare of animals. The Institute is especially dedicated to researching and publicizing the unique needs of chimpanzees. One of the goals of the Institute is the long-term preservation of chimpanzees living in the wild. Founded in 1977 by Dr. Jane Goodall, the Institute continues to teach people around the world.

R. E. Search, "Jane Goodall Institute," Tribune, 9 September 1997.

Jane Goodall Institute: Dedicated to Wildlife Research

By R. E. Search
Tribune Staff Writer

The Jane Goodall Institute, based in Ridgefield, Connecticut, is a nonprofit organization committed to wildlife research, environmental education, and the conservation and welfare of animals. The Institute is especially dedicated to researching and publicizing the unique needs of chimpanzees. One of the goals of the Institute is the long-term preservation of chimpanzees living in the wild. Founded in 1977 by Dr. Jane Goodall, the Institute continues to teach people around the world.

R. E. Search, "Jane Goodall Institute," Tribune, 9 September 1997.

Jane Goodall

Subtopic 1	Subtopic 2

Subtopic 3	Subtopic 4

Name _____

Jane Goodall

Guided Report 6

Volcanoes

1 Choosing a Topic

1. Define topic. **A topic is the subject of a report.**
2. Introduce volcanoes as the topic of this model report.

2 Formulating Subtopics

1. Define subtopics. **A subtopic is one part of a topic.**
2. Ask the class what kind of things they want to know about volcanoes. Write their questions on the chalkboard or chart paper.
3. Guide the class in organizing their questions into several categories or subtopics.
   Suggested subtopics:
   What Is a Volcano?
   How Volcanoes Form
   Types of Volcanoes
   Where Volcanoes Are Located
4. Write the subtopics on the note-taking transparency or chart.

3 Locating Information

1. Read the information about volcanoes: a report, a list of interesting facts, and a map.
2. When your students are ready to include additional information sources, model locating information in an encyclopedia, reference or trade book, or on a bookmarked site on the Internet.
3. Remember to list the sources used so that the information will be available for the bibliography. (See sample entries on page 12.)

4 Taking Notes

1. Before reading a passage, ask students to listen for any information that pertains to the chosen subtopics.
2. Read a passage together, either aloud or silently. Start with a single paragraph to increase retention of information.
3. Have students identify information learned and the subtopic(s) to which it pertains.
4. Identify the key words that convey the information and write them on the note taker.
5. Reread the passage as necessary to address each subtopic.

5 Converting Notes to Paragraphs

1. Reread the notes on the chart.
2. Decide as a group which subtopic would make the best beginning point in reporting the information to someone else. There is more than one correct way to do this.
3. Formulate a main idea (topic) sentence to begin the writing. Write the sentence on a transparency or chart. If your students are not ready to do this, suggest a topic sentence they might use.
4. Add sentences that support the main idea and include information from the note taker.
5. Repeat for each subtopic.

6 Responding, Revising, Editing

1. Proofread the finished product with the class.
   • Check first for sense and completeness.
   • Check for spelling, punctuation, and grammar.
2. Make corrections as needed.

7 Producing the Final Copy

1. Decide on a format—handwritten report, word-processed document, or multimedia presentation. (A report form is provided on page 61 if you wish to use it.)
2. Copy the report in the selected format.

8 Including Additional Materials

1. Prepare and add a bibliography.
2. Add charts, graphs, or maps.
3. Add illustrations and graphics.

The Ring of Fire

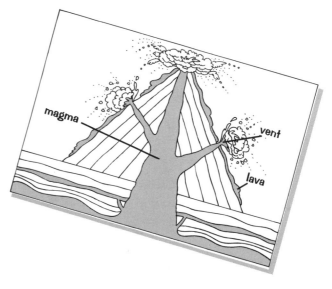

magma

vent

lava

Volcanoes

by E. Ruption

A volcano is a mountain or hill formed around a crack in Earth's crust through which molten rock and other hot materials are pushed out. There are over 500 known active volcanoes in the world and thousands of extinct volcanoes. Volcanoes are found on every continent except Australia. There are about eighty active volcanoes under the oceans. Volcanoes are both terrifying and fascinating. To understand why volcanoes happen, it is necessary to know some things about how Earth is made.

The part of Earth we live on is an eighteen-mile-thick layer of solid rock called the "crust." The crust is made of huge plates that fit together like puzzle pieces. These plates are always moving. Some of Earth's plates move together. One plate may dive under another.

The "mantle" lies beneath the crust. The rock inside the mantle is very hot, but it is solid because of the great pressures on it. When the plates of the crust shift, the friction, or rubbing, of these plates heats the rock and an opening or crack may occur. The opening reduces the pressure and the rock melts, creating a liquid or molten rock called "magma." The magma then flows upward to Earth's surface, either through the crack or through a weak spot in Earth's crust. At the same time, steam and other very hot gases are given off.

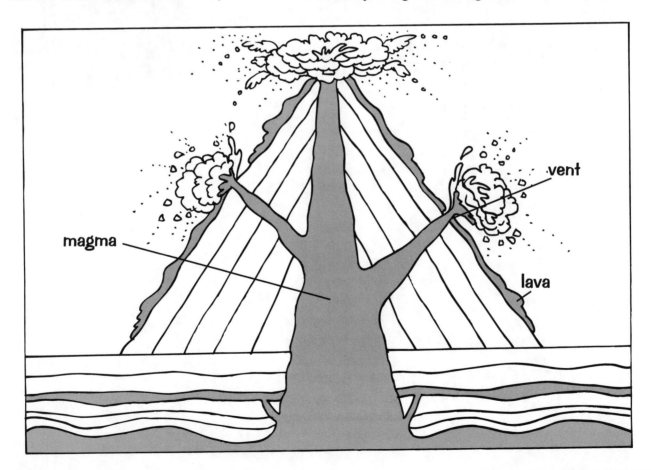

Gas bubbles inside the magma grow bigger and try to escape as the molten rock gets closer to Earth's surface. When the gas bubbles can't be held back any longer, the volcano erupts, and the magma that comes out of it is called "lava." Imagine shaking a soda bottle until the gas inside blows the cap off. That is a little like a volcanic eruption. If the magma is runny and the gas can escape easily, the eruption is gentle. But if the magma is thick, the gas has to build up more pressure to escape. Then the eruption is explosive.

During an explosive eruption, pieces of rock are thrown from the volcano. Scientists call these "pyroclasts." The smallest pyroclasts are called ash. Ash is often hurled high into the atmosphere by the force of the eruption. Larger rocks, about walnut size, are called "lapilli," an Italian word that means "little stones." The largest pyroclasts are called "blocks" if they are solid and "bombs" if they are molten.

Volcanic mountains are made of ash, lava, and rocks that are deposited by each eruption of the volcano. The lava may run for some distance or it may pile up near the volcano, making the mountain larger.

There are different kinds of volcanoes.

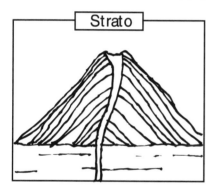

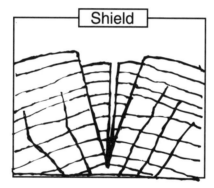

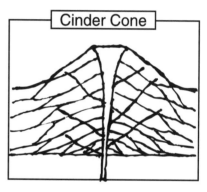

Stratovolcanoes (also called composite volcanoes) are cone-shaped. They are built of layers of pyroclasts. Stratovolcanoes are usually formed from eruptions that have had both quiet and explosive periods. Layers of lava alternate with cinders or ash. Fujiyama in Japan and Mt. Rainier in Washington are examples of stratovolcanoes.

Shield volcanoes are usually formed from quiet eruptions in which the lava spreads out to form a broad base and gentle slopes. Mauna Loa in Hawaii is an example of a shield volcano.

Cinder cone volcanoes are usually formed from explosive eruptions. They have a fairly narrow base and steep slopes. Paricutin in Mexico is an example of a cinder cone volcano formation.

Ruption, E. "Report on Volcanoes." Geology Today (August 1998): pages 79–83.

The Ring of Fire

Millions of years ago volcanoes were found in all parts of the world. Today there are over 800 active volcanoes on Earth's surface. They are located mainly in mountainous regions and under oceans. The ones surrounding the Pacific Ocean form what is known as the "Ring of Fire." Some of them are active—erupting regularly; some of them are dormant—quiet; and some of them are extinct—no activity.

"Ring of Fire Map." <u>Nature's Disasters</u>. Sydney: Earth Watch Press, 1994.

 Guided Report Writing • EMC 732

Fascinating Facts about...
Volcanoes

Fact!! On February 20, 1943, a crack appeared in a cornfield in Mexico. This was the birth of a new volcano named Paricutin. Within a week it grew 500 feet (152 m) and by February 1952, it was 1,350 feet (411 m) high.

Fact!! Mauna Kea, a volcano in Hawaii, is 33,000 feet (10,058 m) high when it is measured from top to bottom, but only the top 14,000 feet (4267 m) stand out above the sea.

Fact!! Lava can move as fast as 40 miles (64 kph) per hour, but it usually flows at no more than 10 miles (16 kph) per hour.

Fact!! Mt. Pinatubo in the Philippines was the site of the largest volcanic explosion of the twentieth century. In June of 1991, 20 million tons (18 metric tons) of gas and ash were shot into the stratosphere, creating a global haze that lowered temperatures half a degree Fahrenheit (about one-fourth of a degree Celsius) for the next 3 to 4 years.

Fact!! Three-fourths of the world's active volcanoes lie within the Ring of Fire—an area where the plates underlying the Pacific Ocean meet the underlying plates of the surrounding continents.

Fact!! In 1963 an underwater eruption in the Atlantic Ocean formed a volcanic island near Iceland. It was named Surtsey after a legendary Icelandic giant.

Fact!! In 1980 Mount Saint Helens in Washington exploded with five hundred times as much energy as the atomic bombs that were dropped on Hiroshima.

Fact!! Crater Lake, 2,000 feet deep (610 m), is the deepest lake in North America. It was formed 7,000 years ago when Mount Mazama in Oregon erupted. The entire mountaintop collapsed, creating a huge crater called a "caldera." Over thousands of years the crater has filled with water.

Magma, H. Exploding News. Seattle: Science Learning, 1994.

Name_____

VOLCANOES

Subtopic 1	Subtopic 2	Subtopic 3

 Guided Report Writing • EMC 732

Volcano Report Form

1. Copy the volcano report. Use as many copies of
   this form as you need.
2. Cut out the pages.
3. Trace and cut out a construction
   paper cover the same
   shape as the report pages.
4. Staple the pages inside
   the cover.
5. Add tissue paper strips
   to represent fire
   and lava.

Kelp Forests

Advance Preparation

1. Reproduce the information about kelp forests on pages 64–67. Include additional sources from your library and the Internet if desired.

2. Reproduce the note taker on page 68 as a transparency or create a large chart on butcher paper.

1 Choosing a Topic

1. Define topic. **A topic is the subject of a report.**
2. Introduce kelp forests as the topic of this model report.

2 Formulating Subtopics

1. Define subtopics. **A subtopic is one part of a topic.**
2. Ask the class what kinds of things they want to know about kelp forests. Write their questions on the chalkboard or chart paper.
3. Guide the class in organizing their questions into several categories or subtopics.
   Suggested subtopics:
   What is a kelp forest?
   Where are kelp forests found?
   What lives in a kelp forest?
4. Write the subtopics on the note-taking transparency or chart.

3 Locating Information

1. Read the information about kelp forests: a textbook chapter and an aquarium brochure.
2. When your students are ready to include additional information sources, model locating information in an encyclopedia, reference or trade book, or on a bookmarked site on the Internet.
3. Remember to list the sources used so that the information will be available for the bibliography. (See sample entries on page 12.)

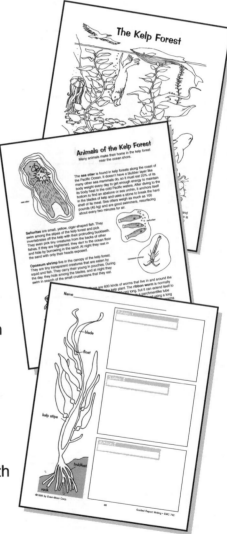

4 Taking Notes

1. Before reading a passage, ask students to listen for any information that pertains to the chosen subtopics.
2. Read a passage together, either aloud or silently. Start with a single paragraph to increase retention of information.
3. Have students identify information learned and the subtopic(s) to which it pertains.
4. Identify the key words that convey the information and write them on the note taker.
5. Reread the passage as necessary to address each subtopic.

5 Converting Notes to Paragraphs

1. Reread the notes on the chart.
2. Decide as a group which subtopic would make the best beginning point in reporting the information to someone else. There is more than one correct way to do this.
3. Formulate a main idea (topic) sentence to begin the writing. Write the sentence on a transparency or chart. If your students are not ready to do this, suggest a topic sentence they might use.
4. Add sentences that support the main idea and include information from the note taker.
5. Repeat for each subtopic.

6 Responding, Revising, Editing

1. Proofread the finished product with the class.
   - Check first for sense and completeness.
   - Check for spelling, punctuation, and grammar.
2. Make corrections as needed.

7 Producing the Final Copy

1. Decide on a format—handwritten report, word-processed document, or multimedia presentation. (A report form is provided on page 69 if you wish to use it.)
2. Copy the report in the selected format.

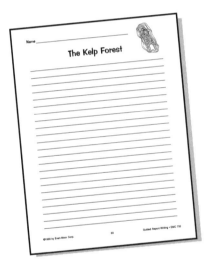

8 Including Additional Materials

1. Prepare and add a bibliography.
2. Add charts, graphs, or maps.
3. Add illustrations and graphics.

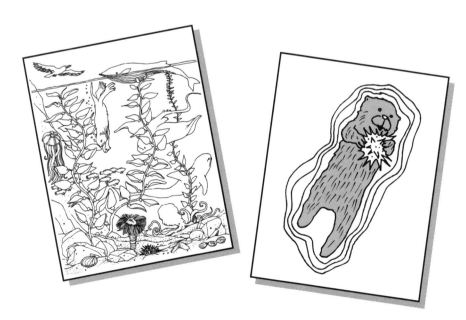

The Kelp Forest

The kelp forest is one of many specialized ecosystems of the ocean. Kelp forests are found along coastlines where there are hard surfaces to which the kelp can attach itself, and where there are plenty of nutrients, moderate water motion, and clear, cool ocean water. Kelp is the name for a group of large seaweeds, or giant brown algae, that sometimes grow over 100 feet tall. There are 20 different species of kelp that grow along the coast of California alone.

A kelp plant has three important parts: the holdfast, the stipe, and the blades. The holdfast attaches the kelp to the rock. It is rootlike, but it is not actually a root because it doesn't gather water and nutrients and send them up to the plant. It simply "holds fast" to a rock and secures the kelp so that it will not be swept away by the ocean tides.

Kelp

The stipe is like a stem. It is tough but flexible. It is the anchor line, a vital connection between the holdfast and the blades. Food moves through the stipe from the blades to the bottom of the plant. The stipe has floats—hollow bumps filled with air that provide buoyancy. The floats pull the blades to the surface where they can get more sunlight. One type of kelp, the giant kelp, has one float for each blade. Another type, the bull kelp, has one big float for the whole plant.

The blade looks like a leaf. It absorbs water, carbon dioxide, and other chemicals. Then it uses energy from sunlight to convert those elements into oxygen and food for the plant. This process is called photosynthesis and is an important function of all green plants. The blade also produces spores that, in turn, produce new kelp plants.

In the kelp forest, animals and plants seem to live in layers. Near the surface, the kelp canopy floats in the water. The juvenile stages of many invertebrates, such as hydroids and bryozoans, hide among the blades. Sea otters anchor themselves while they sleep by wrapping up in the kelp. Along the stipes, the turban snails move up and down. Plankton, tiny drifting plants and animals, float by. Here there are many slender fish like the señoritas. The holdfast is home to a community of small sea creatures such as snails, brittle stars, worms, and hermit crabs. These creatures nibble the stubby branches of the holdfast and live in relative safety inside it.

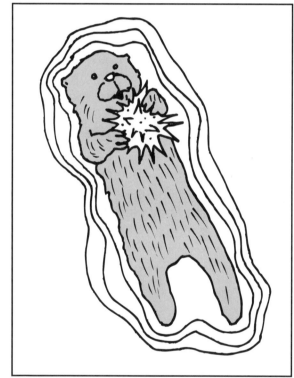

Otters balance food, such as abalone, on their stomachs and use a rock to crack the shells open.

Underwater, I. C. <u>Nature's Ecosystems</u>. Atlantis: Ocean Inc., 1996.

Animals of the Kelp Forest

Many animals make their home in the kelp forest
near the ocean shore.

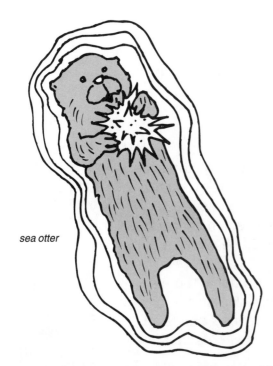

sea otter

The **sea otter** is found in kelp forests along the coast of the Pacific Ocean. It doesn't have a blubber layer like many other sea mammals do, so it must eat 25% of its body weight every day to get enough energy to maintain its body heat in the cold Pacific waters. After diving to the bottom to find an abalone or sea urchin, it anchors itself in the blades of kelp and uses a stone to break the hard shell of its meal. Sea otters weigh as much as 100 pounds (45 kg) and are good swimmers, resurfacing about every two minutes for air.

Señoritas are small, yellow, cigar-shaped fish. They swim among the stipes of the kelp forest and pick invertebrates off the kelp with their protruding buckteeth. They even pick tiny creatures from the backs of other fishes. If they are frightened, they dart to the ocean floor and hide by burrowing in the sand. At night they rest in the sand with only their heads exposed.

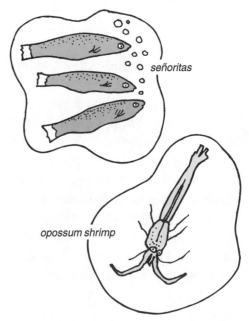

señoritas

opossum shrimp

Opossum shrimp live in the canopy of the kelp forest. They are tiny transparent creatures that are eaten by squid and fish. They carry their young in pouches. During the day, they hide among the blades, and at night they swim in search of the small crustaceans that they eat.

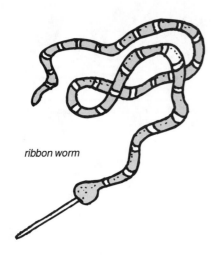

ribbon worm

There are 600 kinds of worms that live in and around the holdfast of the kelp plant. The **ribbon worm** is normally about eight inches (20 cm) long, but it can extend itself to a yard (about a meter). It lives in a parchmentlike tube anchored among the algae. It gathers food using a long tonguelike appendage called a proboscis. Ribbon worms are night carnivores. They eat other worms, small fish, mollusks, and small crabs.

Guided Report Writing • EMC 732

The underside of a **sea star** is covered with hundreds of tube feet powered by a fluid-filled hydraulic system. The tube feet act like suction cups, pushing and pulling to move the star. Sea stars seem rigid, but the flexibility of their arms is shown when a wave flips one over. The arms curl under, while the tiny tube feet get a grip on a rock. Slowly the animal rights itself. A sea star eats mollusks, such as mussels and clams. Its mouth is located at the center of its body on the underside. Sea stars can grow a new arm if one is damaged or cut off. Some sea star relatives look nothing like the sea star.

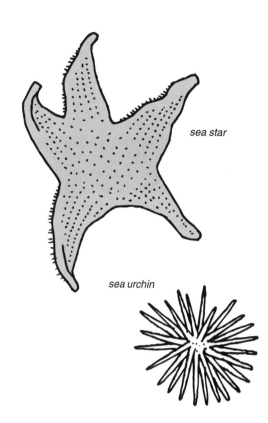

sea star

The **sea urchin** starts out as a star, but its rays fold up over its top and grow together. Its long spines grow and it looks like a pincushion.

sea urchin

sea cucumber

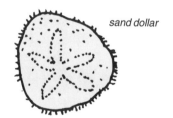

sand dollar

The **sea cucumber** starts out as a star, but its rays never grow. The central part of its body grows into a long tube. Its five rows of little tube feet are all on one side of its body.

The **sand dollar** starts out as a star. Its rays bend up and grow together, but then flatten down. It grows short, hairlike spines around its circular shape.

"I Love Fish Aquarium." <u>Visitor's Guidebook</u>. 1994.

 Guided Report Writing • EMC 732

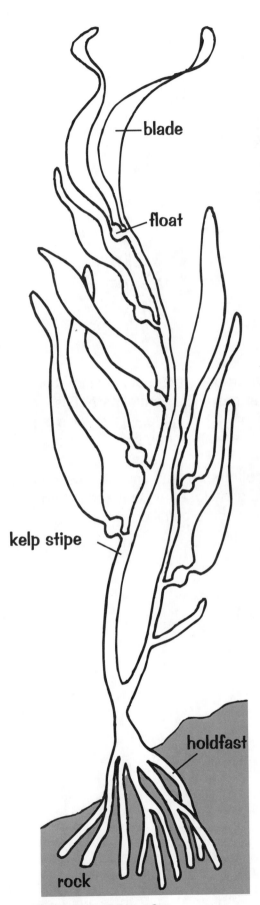

blade

float

kelp stipe

holdfast

rock

Subtopic 1

Subtopic 2

Subtopic 3

Guided Report Writing • EMC 732

Name_____

The Kelp Forest

Guided Report 8

Recycling

Advance Preparation

1. Reproduce the information about recycling on pages 72–74. Include additional sources from your library and the Internet if desired.
2. Reproduce the note taker on page 75 as a transparency or create a large chart on butcher paper. Be sure to reuse paper or charts that have been used before.

1 Choosing a Topic

1. Define topic. **A topic is the subject of a report.**
2. Introduce recycling as the topic of this model report.

2 Formulating Subtopics

1. Define subtopics. **A subtopic is one part of a topic.**
2. Ask the class what kinds of things they want to know about recycling. Write their questions on the chalkboard or chart paper.
3. Guide the class in organizing their questions into several categories or subtopics.
   Suggested subtopics:
   - Why Recycling Is Important
   - Different Kinds of Recycling
   - Practical Ways to Recycle
4. Write the subtopics on the note-taking transparency or chart.

3 Locating Information

1. Read the information about recycling: a flyer, a graph, and a newsletter.
2. When your students are ready to include additional information sources, model locating information in an encyclopedia, reference or trade book, or on a bookmarked site on the Internet.
3. Remember to list the sources used so that the information will be available for the bibliography. (See sample entries on page 12.)

4 Taking Notes

1. Before reading a passage, ask students to listen for any information that pertains to the chosen subtopics.
2. Read a passage together, either aloud or silently. Start with a single paragraph to increase retention of information.
3. Have students identify information learned and the subtopic(s) to which it pertains.
4. Identify the key words that convey the information and write them on the note taker.
5. Reread the passage as necessary to address each subtopic.

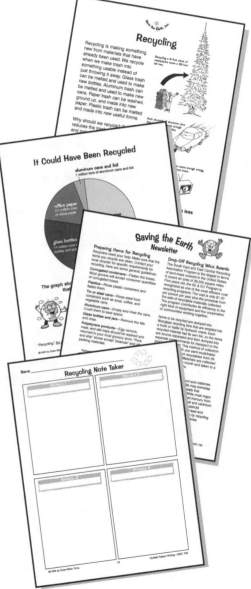

5 Converting Notes to Paragraphs

1. Reread the notes on the chart.
2. Decide as a group which subtopic would make the best beginning point in reporting the information to someone else. There is more than one correct way to do this.
3. Formulate a main idea (topic) sentence to begin the writing. Write the sentence on a transparency or chart. If your students are not ready to do this, suggest a topic sentence they might use.
4. Add sentences that support the main idea and include information from the note taker.
5. Repeat for each subtopic.

6 Responding, Revising, Editing

1. Proofread the finished product with the class.
   • Check first for sense and completeness.
   • Check for spelling, punctuation, and grammar.
2. Make corrections as needed.

7 Producing the Final Copy

1. Decide on a format—handwritten report, word-processed document, or multimedia presentation. (A report form is provided on page 76 if you wish to use it.)
2. Copy the report in the selected format.

8 Including Additional Materials

1. Prepare and add a bibliography.
2. Add charts, graphs, or maps.
3. Add illustrations and graphics.

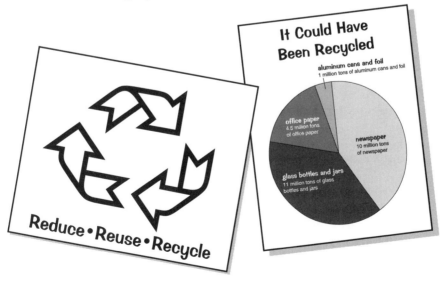

Recycling

Recycling is making something new from materials that have already been used. We recycle when we make trash into something usable instead of just throwing it away. Glass trash can be melted and used to make new bottles. Aluminum trash can be melted and used to make new cans. Paper trash can be washed, ground up, and made into new paper. Plastic trash can be melted and made into new useful forms.

Why should we recycle? Recycling reduces the trash put in landfills and incinerators. One half of the garbage that is thrown out could be recycled. If we recycle, we can use the same materials over and over again. This saves energy because it takes less energy to turn recycled materials into new products than it does to make something from scratch.

Recycling a 6-foot stack of newspapers saves a 35-foot tall tree.

Each six-pack of aluminum cans that is recycled saves enough energy to drive five miles

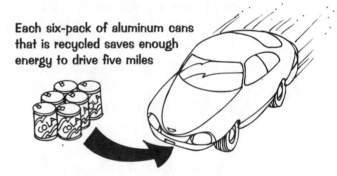

Recycling one aluminum can saves enough energy to run a television set for three hours.

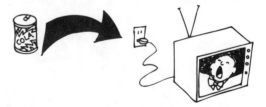

Recycling saves natural resources and energy, creates less pollution, and helps keep air and water clean.

It Could Have Been Recycled

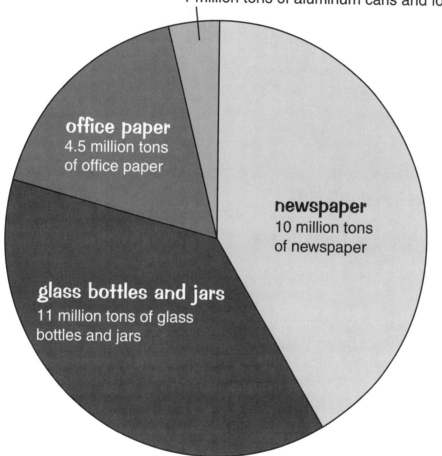

aluminum cans and foil
1 million tons of aluminum cans and foil

office paper
4.5 million tons
of office paper

newspaper
10 million tons
of newspaper

glass bottles and jars
11 million tons of glass
bottles and jars

The graph shows the quantities of recyclable materials that Americans threw away in 1900.

• Recycling one glass jar saves enough energy to light a 100-watt light bulb for four hours.

• Recycling one 12-ounce can saves six ounces of gasoline, and results in 95% less air pollution and 97% less water pollution than creating one new aluminum can from raw materials.

• Manufacturing new paper products from waste paper rather than wood pulp uses at least a third less energy and cuts air pollution by 74%.

"Recycling." <u>An Almanac</u>. 1999.

 Guided Report Writing • EMC 732

Saving the Earth
Newsletter

Preparing Items for Recycling

Recyclers need your help. Make sure that the items you recycle are clean. Contact your local recycler for specific requirements for recycling. Here are some general guidelines:

Corrugated containers—Flatten the boxes. Most grocers will accept consumer quantities of corrugated boxes.

Plastics—Rinse plastic containers and flatten them.

Tin or steel cans—Rinse steel food containers such as soup, coffee, and vegetable cans.

Aluminum cans—Empty and rinse the cans. Crush them to save space.

Glass bottles and jars—Remove the lids and rinse.

Polystyrene products—Egg cartons, meat, and deli trays should be washed and returned to your local grocery store. "Pack and ship" stores accept "peanuts" and other packing materials.

Drop-Off Recycling Wins Awards

The South East and East Central Recycling Association Program is the largest in terms of land mass covered in the United States. It covers an area of 36,200 square miles. Five years old, the SE & EC Program is recognized as one of the most efficient rural recycling programs. The cost is only $1.20 per person per year plus the proceeds from the sale of recyclable materials collected. The program contributes its efficiency to the right kind of equipment and the cooperation of communities working together.

Items to be recycled are dumped into fiberglass recycling bins that are emptied into a truck or trailer by hydraulic crane. Each recycled material has its own bin, so the items are source separated and then dumped into separate compartments for transport to the processing center. This method of collection allows one man with one semi-truck/trailer combination to collect recyclables from 56 sites in 13 counties. Materials are collected from each site once a month and taken to a regional processing site.

Recycle Batteries

Recycle your household and auto batteries. Batteries thrown into landfills may someday leak toxic chemicals and metals that contaminate ground water. While most major manufacturers have eliminated mercury from household batteries, both nickel and cadmium are common in heavy-duty household batteries. Auto batteries contain lead and sulfuric acid. Preventing pollution by recycling batteries makes environmental sense.

Saving the Earth Newsletter. Saving America Recycling Association, 1984.

Recycling Note Taker

Subtopic 1

Subtopic 2

Subtopic 3

Subtopic 4

Recycling

_____
_____
_____
_____
_____
_____
_____
_____
_____
_____
_____
_____
_____
_____
_____
_____
_____
_____
_____
_____
_____
_____

Jacques Cousteau

Advance Preparation
1. Reproduce the information about Jacques Cousteau on pages 79–81. Include additional sources from your library and the Internet if desired.
2. Reproduce the note taker on page 82 as a transparency or create a large chart on butcher paper.

1 Choosing a Topic

1. Define topic. **A topic is the subject of a report.**
2. Introduce Jacques Cousteau as the topic of this model report.

2 Formulating Subtopics

1. Define subtopics. **A subtopic is one part of a topic.**
2. Ask the class what kinds of things they want to know about Mr. Cousteau. Write their questions on the chalkboard or chart paper.
3. Guide the class in organizing their questions into several categories or subtopics.
   Suggested subtopics:
   Childhood
   Accomplishments
   Importance in History
4. Write the subtopics on the note-taking transparency or chart.

3 Locating Information

1. Read the information about Jacques Cousteau: a magazine article.
2. When your students are ready to include additional information sources, model locating information in an encyclopedia, reference or trade book, or on a bookmarked site on the Internet.
3. Remember to list the sources used so that the information will be available for the bibliography. (See sample entries on page 12.)

4 Taking Notes

1. Before reading a passage, ask students to listen for any information that pertains to the chosen subtopics.
2. Read a passage together, either aloud or silently. Start with a single paragraph to increase retention of information.
3. Have students identify information learned and the subtopic(s) to which it pertains.
4. Identify the key words that convey the information and write them on the note taker.
5. Reread the passage as necessary to address each subtopic.

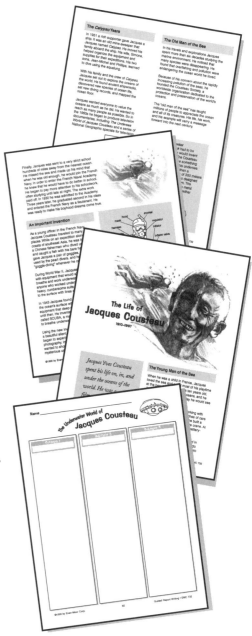

5 Converting Notes to Paragraphs

1. Reread the notes on the chart.
2. Decide as a group which subtopic would make the best beginning point in reporting the information to someone else. There is more than one correct way to do this.
3. Formulate a main idea (topic) sentence to begin the writing. Write the sentence on a transparency or chart. If your students are not ready to do this, suggest a topic sentence they might use.
4. Add sentences that support the main idea using information from the note taker.
5. Repeat for each subtopic.

6 Responding, Revising, Editing

1. Proofread the finished product with the class.
   • Check first for sense and completeness.
   • Check for spelling, punctuation, and grammar.
2. Make corrections as needed.

7 Producing the Final Copy

1. Decide on a format—handwritten report, word-processed document, or multimedia presentation. (A report form is provided on page 83 if you wish to use it.)
2. Copy the report in the selected format.

8 Including Additional Materials

1. Prepare and add a bibliography.
2. Add charts, graphs, or maps.
3. Add illustrations and graphics.

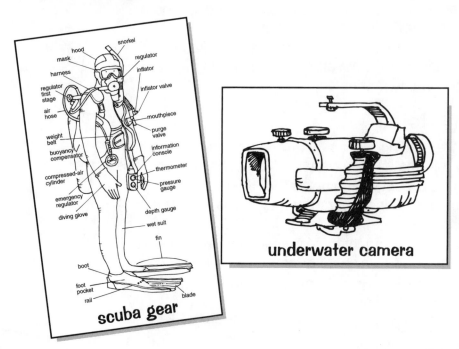

scuba gear

underwater camera

The Life of
Jacques Cousteau
1910–1997

Jacques Yves Cousteau spent his life on, in, and under the oceans of the world. He was a filmmaker, a writer, an oceanographer, an inventor, a sailor, and an environmentalist.

By D.P. Sea

The Young Man of the Sea

When he was a child in France, Jacques loved the sea and spent most of his playtime at the beach. Before he was ten years old, Jacques had seen several oceans, and he promised himself that someday he would see them all.

Young Jacques also enjoyed working with machines. He liked making sketches of cars and boats. When he was eleven he built a fourteen-foot tall model of a marine crane. At thirteen, he built a three-foot long battery-powered automobile.

Although he was smart and interested in all sorts of different things, he did not do well in school. He was bored and got into trouble often.

79

Finally, Jacques was sent to a very strict school hundreds of miles away from the nearest ocean. He missed the sea and made up his mind that when he was old enough, he would join the French Navy. In order to enter the French Naval Academy, he knew that he would have to do better in school. He began to pay more attention to his schoolwork, often studying until late at night. The extra work paid off. In 1930 he was admitted to the Academy. Three years later, he graduated second in his class and entered the French Navy as a lieutenant. He was ready to make his boyhood dreams come true.

An Important Invention

As a young officer in the French Navy, Jacques Cousteau traveled to many faraway places. While on an expedition along the coasts of southeast Asia, he was impressed by a Chinese fisherman who dived underwater and caught a fish with his bare hands. A friend gave Jacques a pair of goggles, like those used by the pearl divers, and he began "goggle-diving" whenever he could.

During World War II, Jacques experimented with equipment that would allow him to breathe and work underwater. At that time, anyone who worked underwater had to wear heavy, cumbersome suits and be connected to the surface with lines and air hoses.

In 1943 Jacques found a way to stay under the ocean's surface without all the clumsy equipment that deep-sea divers had used up until then. He invented the aqualung, now called SCUBA, a machine that allows a diver to breathe underwater while swimming freely.

Using the new invention, Jacques discovered a beautiful silent world under the sea. He also began to experiment with underwater photography, including motion pictures. He wanted to show everyone the beautiful and mysterious undersea world that he loved.

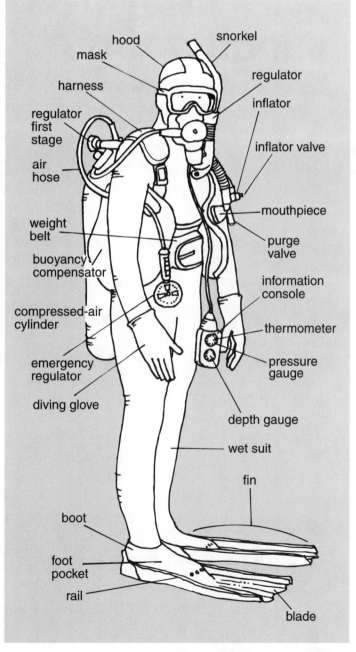

The *Calypso* Years

In 1951 a rich supporter gave Jacques a ship. It was an old mine-sweeper that Jacques named *Calypso*. He moved his family aboard the ship. His wife, Simone, helped organize the equipment and supplies for their expeditions. His two sons, Jean-Michel and Phillipe, learned to dive using the aqualung.

With his family and the crew of *Calypso*, Jacques set out to explore the oceans of the world. He found ancient shipwrecks, discovered new species of ocean life, set new diving records, and mapped the ocean floor.

Jacques wanted everyone to value the oceans as much as he did. He wanted to reach as many people as possible. So in the 1960s he began to produce television documentaries, including *The Undersea World of Jacques Cousteau* and a series of National Geographic specials for television.

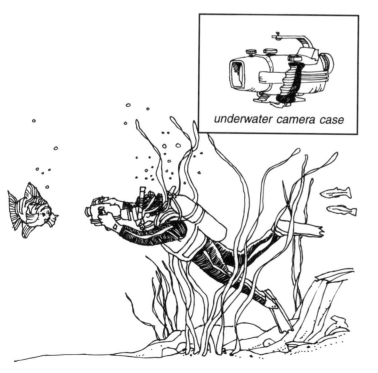

underwater camera case

The Old Man of the Sea

In his travels and explorations Jacques spent more than six decades studying the marine environment. He noticed that many species were disappearing. He found that overfishing and pollution were endangering the ocean world he loved.

Because of his concern about the rapidly increasing pollution of the seas, he founded the Cousteau Society, a worldwide organization dedicated to the protection and preservation of the world's oceans.

The "old man of the sea" has taught millions of people to appreciate the ocean and all of its creatures. His life, his work, and his example will carry a message forward into the next century.

Cousteau the Inventor

Whenever a new task had to be performed, Cousteau would invent a way to get it done. The Cousteau Diving Saucer looks like something out of science fiction. This undersea vehicle has made more than a thousand dives to depths of 300 meters (1,000 feet). Cousteau also designed a "house" on the sea bottom. The Conshelf is a series of large metal and glass bubbles joined together with tubes.

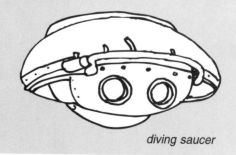

diving saucer

Sea, D. P. "Jacques Cousteau." <u>Underwater Digest</u> (January 1999): pages 30–33.

The Underwater World of
Jacques Cousteau

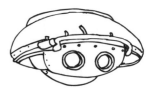

Subtopic 1	Subtopic 2	Subtopic 3

Jacques Cousteau

Chimpanzees

Advance Preparation
1. Reproduce the information about chimpanzees on pages 86–89. Include additional sources from your library and the Internet if desired.
2. Reproduce the note taker on page 90 as a transparency or create a large chart on butcher paper.

1 Choosing a Topic

1. Define topic. **A topic is the subject of a report.**
2. Introduce chimpanzees as the topic of this model report.

2 Formulating Subtopics

1. Define subtopics. **A subtopic is one part of a topic.**
2. Ask the class what kinds of things they want to know about chimpanzees. Write their questions on the chalkboard or chart paper.
3. Guide the class in organizing their questions into several categories or subtopics.
   Suggested subtopics:
   What they look like
   What they eat
   What they do
   Where they live
4. Write the subtopics on the note-taking transparency or chart.

3 Locating Information

1. Read the information about chimpanzees: a textbook and an animal trading card.
2. When your students are ready to include additional information sources, model locating information in an encyclopedia, reference or trade book, or on a bookmarked site on the Internet.
3. Remember to list the sources used so that the information will be available for the bibliography. (See sample entries on page 12.)

4 Taking Notes

1. Before reading a passage, ask students to listen for any information that pertains to the chosen subtopics.
2. Read a passage together, either aloud or silently. Start with a single paragraph to increase retention of information.
3. Have students identify information learned and the subtopic(s) to which it pertains.
4. Identify the key words that convey the information and write them on the note taker.
5. Reread the passage as necessary to address each subtopic.

5 Converting Notes to Paragraphs

1. Reread the notes on the chart.
2. Decide as a group which subtopic would make the best beginning point in reporting the information to someone else. There is more than one correct way to do this.
3. Formulate a main idea (topic) sentence to begin the writing. Write the sentence on a transparency or chart. If your students are not ready to do this, suggest a topic sentence they might use.
4. Add sentences that support the main idea using information from the note taker.
5. Repeat for each subtopic.

6 Responding, Revising, Editing

1. Proofread the finished product with the class.
   - Check first for sense and completeness.
   - Check for spelling, punctuation, and grammar.
2. Make corrections as needed.

7 Producing the Final Copy

1. Decide on a format—handwritten report, word-processed document, or multimedia presentation. (A report form is provided on page 91 if you wish to use it.)
2. Copy the report in the selected format.

8 Including Additional Materials

1. Prepare and add a bibliography.
2. Add charts, graphs, or maps.
3. Add illustrations and graphics.

Watching Chimpanzees

Young chimpanzees are a lot like human children. They laugh and play. They wrestle with their friends. They like to be tickled and hugged. They are busy learning about their world from older chimpanzees. Would you like to know more about this delightful primate? Read on.

Life Among the Trees

Chimpanzees have bodies made for climbing and swinging from trees. They have long arms for reaching for branches. Their feet and hands are made to grab and hang onto branches. For safety, they make nests in trees and curl up for the night. Young chimps sleep in the same nest with their moms.

Chimpanzee Communities

Although chimpanzees live in communities as large as 80 members, they spend a lot of time in small groups. The small groups move around looking for food and grooming each other. (Grooming means moving their fingers through each other's hair to clean the skin.) Grooming helps keep the chimps calm and friendly.

Each chimp has a place, called a rank, in the community. The top male is not always the biggest chimp or the strongest chimp. It is usually the smartest chimp. As long as all of the chimps know their rank, they seldom fight. They do make a lot of noise and wave their arms around. They will fight for food or mates. Females will fight to protect their young.

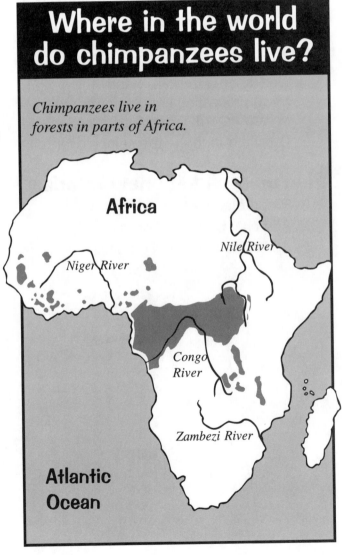

Where in the world do chimpanzees live?

Chimpanzees live in forests in parts of Africa.

Africa

Nile River

Niger River

Congo River

Zambezi River

Atlantic Ocean

Apes come in various sizes ...

from the tiny lemur to the large gorilla. The chimpanzee is one of the larger apes.

lemur
1½ feet tall
(45.5 cm)

chimpanzee
4 feet tall
(1.25 m)

gorilla
5 feet tall
(1.5 m)

Can chimps talk?

Can you tell how your friends are feeling just by looking at their faces? Chimpanzees cannot speak the way we do. But they can communicate. They use their whole bodies to let other chimps know what they feel. When they are scared, they will hold hands or hug. They show friendship by hugging and kissing when they meet. A chimp will put out a hand to beg for food from another chimp.

They also use different calls to mean different things. They use calls to warn others of danger. They use calls that mean they are happy or not happy.

What does a hungry chimp eat?

Chimpanzees usually eat fruit and leaves. They will also eat eggs and insects. They will sometimes hunt other animals for meat.

Chimps know how to use twigs as tools for finding food. They take the leaves off the twig and poke it into a termite nest or a beehive. They eat the insects or the honey that sticks to the twig.

Rock-a-Bye Baby Chimp

Chimpanzees in the wild are good mothers. Chimpanzees are mammals. Like all mammals, baby chimpanzees drink their mother's milk. Young chimps stay with their mothers for many years. Chimps take a long time to grow up (about 5 years). They have a lot to learn about taking care of themselves. They learn how to find food, build nests, avoid danger, and fight by watching and playing with other chimps.

Danger! Danger!

Chimpanzees are in danger of disappearing in the wild. There used to be millions of them; now there are fewer than 200,000.

Chimps are killed by people and animals. They are hunted to sell to zoos, circuses, and labs. Their forest homes are being destroyed to build farms, villages, and roads.

It is important to try to find ways to save the chimps that still live in the wild. There need to be safe parks and nature preserves where they can live.

Do you know her name?

Jane Goodall has studied the chimpanzees of Gombe for 30 years. Her careful notes and observations have helped scientists around the world have a better understanding of animal behavior.

Chimpanzees

Chimpanzees live in rainforests and tree-covered savannas where they spend about one-third of their time in the trees.

They spend four hours a day eating fruit. Each evening before they build their sleeping nest in a tree, they eat a meal of leaves and shoots. If plants aren't available, chimpanzees will eat seeds, blossoms, resin, and even bark. Sometimes the chimpanzee will add meat to its diet in the form of termites, ants, and small animals.

Chimpanzees are highly intelligent and communicate with each other through gestures and movements. The chimpanzee language also has a lot of different sounds including grunts, screeches, and hoots.

Chimpanzee. Animal Trading Cards. 1998.

Chimpanzees

Chimpanzees live in rainforests and tree-covered savannas where they spend about one-third of their time in the trees.

They spend four hours a day eating fruit. Each evening before they build their sleeping nest in a tree, they eat a meal of leaves and shoots. If plants aren't available, chimpanzees will eat seeds, blossoms, resin, and even bark. Sometimes the chimpanzee will add meat to its diet in the form of termites, ants, and small animals.

Chimpanzees are highly intelligent and communicate with each other through gestures and movements. The chimpanzee language also has a lot of different sounds including grunts, screeches, and hoots.

Chimpanzee. Animal Trading Cards. 1998.

Chimpanzees

Chimpanzees live in rainforests and tree-covered savannas where they spend about one-third of their time in the trees.

They spend four hours a day eating fruit. Each evening before they build their sleeping nest in a tree, they eat a meal of leaves and shoots. If plants aren't available, chimpanzees will eat seeds, blossoms, resin, and even bark. Sometimes the chimpanzee will add meat to its diet in the form of termites, ants, and small animals.

Chimpanzees are highly intelligent and communicate with each other through gestures and movements. The chimpanzee language also has a lot of different sounds including grunts, screeches, and hoots.

Chimpanzee. Animal Trading Cards. 1998.

Chimpanzees

Chimpanzees live in rainforests and tree-covered savannas where they spend about one-third of their time in the trees.

They spend four hours a day eating fruit. Each evening before they build their sleeping nest in a tree, they eat a meal of leaves and shoots. If plants aren't available, chimpanzees will eat seeds, blossoms, resin, and even bark. Sometimes the chimpanzee will add meat to its diet in the form of termites, ants, and small animals.

Chimpanzees are highly intelligent and communicate with each other through gestures and movements. The chimpanzee language also has a lot of different sounds including grunts, screeches, and hoots.

Chimpanzee. Animal Trading Cards. 1998.

Guided Report Writing • EMC 732

CHIMPS

	Source 1	Source 2
SUBTOPIC 1		
SUBTOPIC 2		
SUBTOPIC 3		

Name_____

C H I M P S

91

Name _____

Checklist for Writing a Report

Mark each box when the step is completed.

☐ **My topic is:**

_____

teacher check

☐ **My subtopics are:**

_____

_____

_____

teacher check

☐ **My sources of information are:**

_____

_____

_____

_____

teacher check

☐ **Prepare note taker:**

_____ I entered information about the source.

_____ I wrote subtopics on the note taker.

teacher check

☐ **I have read and taken notes on:**

_____ Source 1

_____ Source 2

_____ Source 3
_____

☐ **My rough draft has been written and edited for:**

_____ ideas that make sense and are in the proper order

_____ paragraphing

_____ capitalization

_____ punctuation

_____ spelling

☐ **My rough draft has been proofread by someone else for:**
_____

_____ ideas that make sense and are in the proper order

_____ paragraphing

_____ capitalization

_____ punctuation

_____ spelling

proofer's name:

☐ **Final copy finished.**
_____

☐ **Final copy proofread.**
_____

_____

Guided Report Writing • EMC 732

Searching for Information on the Internet

The Internet is an excellent source of information. A "bookmark" is a way to mark a site that you've already visited so that you can go there quickly without having to type the site's URL.

As your students become more skilled, they will begin searching for information on their own. When they do, they will use one of two approaches for finding information.

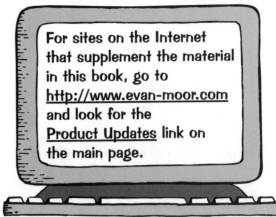

For sites on the Internet that supplement the material in this book, go to http://www.evan-moor.com and look for the **Product Updates** link on the main page.

- The first is to use a **subject directory**. Students are presented with a list of very general subjects by a search engine. Choosing one of these subjects takes the student to another, more specific list where another choice can be made to narrow the search. The process continues until specific Web page links are given. If you are interested in browsing general information, use a subject index instead of a keyword search.

- The quickest and most powerful way to find Internet information is to use a **keyword search**. Using a search engine, you look through a comprehensive database for a specific topic. On the search engine home page, you enter in a box keywords that represent a topic. The result is a list of links containing the terms you entered. Web search engines retrieve information from databases of links to all kinds of information.

Patience, Persistence, and Resourcefulness

You will need to be flexible in your search strategies and in your expectations in order to find useful information with a minimum of frustration.

- Give your modem and your computer time to retrieve the information that you have found.
- Know the requirements of the search engine you are using so that you can structure your query correctly. Check in the help section for instructions specific to the search engine that you are using.
- Try different terms or different search engines until you find the results that you want.

 Guided Report Writing • EMC 732

Evaluating Web Sites

Just as users of print materials must evaluate the source of their information, it is up to the users of the Internet to be critical consumers of information.

As a teacher, it is your job to find the materials, out of the thousands of sites available, that can be useful to you as an educator. The Web contains a wealth of wonderful resources, but it also contains a great deal of misinformation and unevaluated information. So evaluate a Web site just as you would carefully evaluate a print resource. And remember, since Web resources can change so quickly, evaluating them is an ongoing process.

Before you bookmark a site for use with your class, consider the quality of the site.
• Is the site technically reliable?
• Is the site objective and accurate?

An evaluation checklist is provided for you on page 96. "Yes" answers to the checklist questions indicate a high-quality Web page. Include additional questions on the checklist so that it will meet the needs of your classroom.

Remember that hypertext links may lead the user to Web pages of a different quality. Evaluate each Web page independently.

As capable students begin navigating and searching on their own, they will need to evaluate the Internet sites that they find. Model how to use the checklist on page 96 and provide copies for students to use when they visit new sites.

Guided Report Writing • EMC 732

Checklist for Evaluating Web Sites

Site URL:

Where did the information come from?

Is it clear who sponsors the page?	yes	no
Is the purpose of the sponsoring organization given?	yes	no
Is the author of the information given?	yes	no
Are the author's qualifications stated?	yes	no

Is the information accurate?

Are the sources of any factual information listed?	yes	no
Is the information free of grammatical, spelling, and other errors?	yes	no
Are charts and graphs clearly labeled and easy to read?	yes	no

Is the information objective?

Is the information presented as a public service?	yes	no
Is the information free of advertising?	yes	no
Is the information trying to change the opinion of the audience?	yes	no

Is the information current?

Are there dates on the page to tell when it was written?	yes	no
Does the page tell when it was last updated?	yes	no

Is the information complete?

Is the page complete (not under construction)?	yes	no
Are the topics included explored in depth?	yes	no
Is the information appropriate?	yes	no
Is the design of the site easy to understand?	yes	no
Is the material understandable?	yes	no